KU-557-244

Discussion

Ci80
Concrete International 1980

Discussion

The Concrete Society

ANDERSONIAN LIBRARY
★
WITHDRAWN FROM LIBRARY STOCK
►
UNIVERSITY OF STRATHCLYDE

THE CONSTRUCTION PRESS
LANCASTER　　LONDON　　NEW YORK

The Construction Press Ltd, Longman House, Burnt Mill, Harlow, Essex

A subsidiary company of Longman Group Ltd, London
Associated companies, branches and representatives throughout the world

Published in the United States of America by Longman Inc, New York

This collection © Construction Press Ltd, 1981

All rights reserved. No part of this publication may be reproduced, stored
in a retrieval system, or transmitted in any form or by any means, electronic,
mechanical, photocpying, recording, or otherwise, without the prior per-
mission of the copyright owner.

First published 1981

ISBN 0 86095 860 4

Printed by UPS Blackburn Limited, Blackburn, England

D
624.1834
CON

Contents

Lightweight concrete   1

Design considerations for reinforced lightweight concrete   3
A Gerritse

Shear carrying behaviour of lightweight concrete beams as compared to
normal weight concrete beams   23
H R Kirmair

Investigation into sintering coal-mine shales for lightweight aggregate — Part 2 32
H S Wilson

Author's introduction to 'Properties of hardened lightweight aggregate concrete' 48
F D Lydon

Some structures built in France in lightweight concrete   52
M Virlogeux

General discussion   61

Errata (*B Bender*)   85

Sprayed concrete   87

General discussion   89

Errata (*E F Humphries*)   114

Fibrous concrete   115

Applications of glass fibre reinforced concrete in Rumania   117
M Hamalgiu and D Constantinescu

General discussion   128

Errata (*D J Hannant*)   140

Admixtures   141

Mechanisms and effects of air-entrainment in concrete   143
C L Page

Specifications and standards for concrete admixtures — an international review   154
T J Tipler

The use of admixtures in concrete pressure vessels for nuclear plant   189
R Blundell and R D Browne

General discussion   210

Other CI80 volumes   247

PUBLISHER'S NOTE

This volume contains all the papers accepted for presentation at Concrete International 1980 (CI80) which were not included in the four previously published volumes, *Lightweight Concrete*, *Sprayed Concrete*, *Fibrous Concrete* and *Admixtures*, together with a carefully edited version of the oral and written discussion relevant to the five volumes, and a comprehensive list of the contents of the four earlier volumes.

Concrete International 1980, which was held in London on 14—17th April 1980 and which incorporated the Second International Congress on Lightweight Concrete, a Symposium on Sprayed Concrete, a Symposium on Fibrous Concrete and an International Congress on Admixtures, was organised by The American Concrete Institute (ACI), The Cement and Concrete Association (C&CA), the Comité Euro-International du Béton (CEB), the Fédération International de la Précontrainte (FIP), The Institution of Civil Engineers and The Institution of Structural Engineers.

FLOOD DAMAGE
20 JAN 1996

Lightweight concrete

Design considerations for reinforced lightweight concrete

A Gerritse
Hollandsche Beton Groep NV, Netherlands

INTRODUCTION

Cement based structural materials are extensively used in building, because they are cheap, strong (in compression), durable, fire resistant etc.
Some aspects however, are less appreciated and sometimes the common constituents are not or difficult available.

-An example of one of the less appreciated aspects is the relative low tensile capacity. To overcome this a range of provisions are practised to reach a better performance, like steel reinforcement, fibre reinforcement, prestressing and polymer additions.
-The difficulties already arising in some areas due to insufficient gravel or quarry possibilities wil increase in the near future. Solutions by natural or artificial substitutes - which can have at the same time the advantage of solving waste material problems (like fly-ash) - are considered and becoming common practice.

These two introductory remarks already show sufficiently the main background. Cement based structural materials are very versatile and apt to modifications dependent on application, geographical area and so on (1,4).

Therefore the modification known as "lightweight(aggregate) concrete" is on one hand a very rough generalisation because much more characteristics then only the weight have to be considered, on the other hand we should realise that in fact, we should speak about "modified concrete", indicating that each modification inherently brings about different characteristics. This wide range of concretes, with differing characteristics, is to be treated in design and execution as structural concrete, but the varying effects, advantageous or less favourable, have to be known, understood and taken into account.

It is shown history, like the Pantheon in Rome, and in the practice of the last two decades, that using lightweight concretes the advantages are overwhelming whilst the less favourable aspects - like cost per m^3 of mortar - are of minor importance for those engineers really utilising lightweight concretes.
The reluctancy sometimes still there, must be regarded as definitely incorrect and possibly due to insufficient experience, pricing and guidance (or imagination).

Since the use of modified types of structural concrete will increase in future, forced by the need to comply with specific applications, like marine structures, forced by better appraisal of the specific advantages and forced also by environmental reasons, it might be appreciated to review some topics here.

(1) See list of references.

Some preliminary statements should be made first.

-Structural lightweight concrete (and most modified types of concrete in general) should not be treated as a different material. Essentially the same approach applies, but sometimes different characteristics have to be inserted.

-Structural lightweight concrete is not a poor substitute for normal weight - or dense - concrete. It has its own merits, advantages and less favourable characteristics.

-Badly designed lightweight concrete structures do not exist. Any concrete structure designed less properly or with a less appropriate mix often appears to be more sensitive to that if executed in lightweight concrete and improper behaviour will be more pronounced.

In more general terms each modification to the "standard" experience (e.g. relating to cementtype, admixtures, prestressing, lightweight aggregates etc.) requires attention and awareness of the specific characteristics of the material.

Restricting ourselves to the use of structural lightweight concrete - and how to use it - much more characteristics have to be considered then in the word lightweight are enclosed.
A list of items - indicative not limitative - may be:

- price of concrete mix per m^3
- weight or density
- strength (compressive, tensile or in shear)
- Youngs modulus (modulus of deformation)
- coëfficient of linear expansion
- creep and shrinkage behaviour
- weather resistance (e.g. frost damage)
- fire resistance
- mix design and workability (floating, water absorption)
- bond
- thermal and sound insulation properties
- carbonation
- pumpability

A much more extensive review, then possible in the scope of this paper, of the items mentioned is given in the CEB/FIP Manual (2) and the proceedings of C.I.80 will provide additional information.

CODE PROVISIONS

In most countries the use of structural lightweight concrete is covered by code provisions. Structural codes do prescribe design requirements, material classifications, execution recommendations and quality control measures. They are usually accompanied by standards, detailing the requirements for the aggregates.

A different approach can be observed:

a. A complete separate code for the use of lightweight concrete, repeating most structural items, with generalised figures for lightweight concrete (Germany).

b. Additional articles in the concrete code, covering lightweight concrete items; mostly in a generalised form. (Great Britain, Belgium, U.S.A.).

4

c. A separate chapter or booklet stating for which articles or items of the concrete "base" code the different material related "response-figures" have to be established and inserted in the concrete code, (5,6). (CEB and Holland).

The approach mentioned under c - establishing figures for the actual type used - should be preferred. There are so many lightweight concretes possible that general factors are just helpful in understanding and as a rough guide. That is why they are used in the following notes, but for design purposes the particular data for the actual lightweight concrete (or modified concrete) have to be determined.
As an example some of the opening clauses of the Dutch code for lightweight concrete are given (fig.1).
The ratio factors cleary indicate that the structural behaviour of the various types of concrete is essentially the same. This means comparing the specific characteristics of the modified type with those of dense concrete of the same grade. It should be emphasised that this approach is in principle not restricted to lightweight concrete but in fact it is appropriate to any modification, irrelevant wether it is lightweight, special heavy weight, fibre reinforced, re-used concrete debris, polymer-impregnated and so on.
The producer or manufacturer will be obliged to provide the required data in order that the maximum advantages can be exploited.

STRUCTURAL IMPLICATIONS OF LIGHTWEIGHT AGGREGATE

Density
The low density of lightweight (aggregate) concrete is the most commonly known feature. For structural purposes (fresh) densities between 1200 kg/m^3 and 1800 kg/m^3 are attainable, and with those 20 N/mm^2 to 70 N/mm^2 respectively is about the maximum compressive strength to be achieved (fig.2).

Roughly 0.7 m^3 of a m^3 concrete mix consists of aggregates. Of this about 0.5 m^3 is the volume taken by the coarse aggregates. Each mix-design will show slight variations to these figures and in itself especially variations due to gap-graded or continuously graded mixes are certainly important. However, in the context of an indication of weight reduction and its consequences the above mentioned volumes are accurate enough.

Replacing 0.5 m^3 coarse dense aggregate by a lightweight aggregate with a particle density of 800 to 1500 kg/m^3 - leads to a gain in weight of 1000 to 600 kg/m^3 respectively and even by replacing also the fine aggregate (sand) by lightweight another 100 to 200 kg/m^3 can be gained. To certain limits - governed by the coherence of the mortar skeleton - an all lightweight mix reaches the same compressive strenght as the sand lightweight mix. And again to certain limits a sand lightweight mix can reach the same compressive strength as a dense mix with comparable composition.
But here we are touching the basic reasons to different behaviour. It all depends on the deformability of the hardened concrete. This deformability depends on the coherence of the mortar skeleton, the ratio between elastic moduli mortar/aggregate and on the adherence between mortar and aggregate particles (7).
The limitations posed to the mortar-skeleton are reason that an all light-weight concrete is only sensible for the lower grades (up to say 30 N/mm^2).

For structural purposes commonly sand-containing mixes are used. They also provide better workability, less shrinkage and they are somewhat cheaper. Overmore the smaller particles of lightweight aggregate have the highest particle density, so the gain in weight is restricted.

Deformability and internal equilibrium

To understand or even predict the parameters expressing the behaviour of
(lightweight) concrete it is important to understand the transmission of
forces in concrete. This depends as mentioned on the deformability, thus
on the rigidity of the components and on the internal adherence (7).
Aggregate particles "softer" than the surrounding mortar do not participate
fully in the transmission of internal forces.
Table I gives an indication of the deformation moduli of mortar and aggregates. With soft aggregates (E particles < E mortar) transfer of forces is
through the mortar matrix. Failure occuring right through the aggregates.
(fig.3). With stiffer aggregates the stresses in the mortar are reduced.
Failure will occur now by extending initial cracks along the aggregates
(fig.4). Lack of interface bond will decrease the load-capacity in both
cases considerable.

The result of the above is expressed by the compressive capacity and the
shape of the stress-strain diagram of the concrete and - even more
pronounced - by the tensile (splitting) strength and E value of the composite. These consequences are - among others - dealt with by Grübl (8).

The compressive strength is a combination of mortar strength and aggregate
strength. This basic relation is given in fig.5.
In comparing the strength development of a set of mixes, only varying in
aggregate type, Grübl determined the relations for these aggregates (fig.6).
He calls the angle (tan α) the "aggregate parameter", with which - dependent
on the amount of cement - a prediction of strength and characteristics can
be made.
The relations with strengths and stiffness of aggregates and mortar might
be clear, however aggregate "stifness" can only be approximated (2).

Other properties

Most functional parameters of lightweight concrete are dependent as well
from strength/stiffness relations between mortar and aggregate. Due to the
range of aggregate types and mix combinations a vast amount of research
results is available, e.g. in litt. (2.3.10).
With some reserves it is commonly possible to condense them to formula with
a reasonable validity. It has been proved that these properties convenient-
ly can be expressed as function of the density and the compressive strength
(table II).

In spite of all the work done to find formula with a sensible low scatter
(coefficients of variations 10-15%) it remains a requirement to determine
the figures for the applications under review. Only to demonstrate that
fig.7 about the (splitting) tensile strength is given. The values measured
are far out the scope of all the formula. The influence of the curing conditions (moist cured or dry) are predominant in this case. The specification
of the curing conditions in determing a tensile strength value must be
explicitly mentioned in codes or manuals.

Deformation of structural members is an important criterion for design,
especially under service conditions.
Instanteneous deformations are a function of the E value and in the case
of bending deflections also of crack formation. The E value or modulus of
deformation varies from 30-60% of that of a comparable dense concrete grade
due - again - to the internal transfer of forces and the type of aggregate.
Professor de Pauw's formula provides a fairly good basis, also because it
comprises dense concrete.

Long term deformations are effected by creep, shrinkage and percentage of
reinforcement (tension stiffening in case of deflections).
Creep and shrinkage depend on aggregate type, cement quantity and humidity

conditions. The resistance to these volume changes - again - is related
to the aggregate/mortar stiffness. Shrinkage strains will mostly be in the
order of 20-30% more than those of a dense reference concrete. Creep figures are more difficult to understand. The total strain due to long term
compression is considerably higher than that of the dense reference.
However, the creep factor ϕ - indicating the ratio of final deformation to
(initial) elastic deformation - is less (ratio factor $\leqslant$ 1), because the
elastic deformation already followed from the lower E value.
A rough but - in the opinion of the author - handsome indication is:

$$\phi \text{ lightweight} = \frac{\rho}{2400} \phi \text{ dense}$$

Although creep affects the deformation of a structure unfavourable it is not
altogether a disadvantage. Internal stresses due to shrinkage, temperature
differentials and imposed stresses are partly relieved with a reduced risk
of cracking (3).

The stress - strain diagram
Some of the consequences of the stiffness of lightweight aggregates
(E agg $\leqslant$ E mat) for the same concrete grade are:

- lower E value of the composite; roughly $(\frac{\rho}{2400})^2$. E dense.

- different shape of the stress-strain diagram:

  - more or less straight ascending branch

  - sharp decrease in the descending branch after maximum

  - larger strain at ultimate capacity

In (7) this is represented in a schematic diagram choosing ε_u as unity
(fig. 8). In this scheme lightweight aggregate concrete has a low t and
a high C value. This means that the use of a parabolic/rectangular diagram
assumption in calculations is less correct for lightweight concrete.
The actual stress-strain diagram used, does effect strength calculations
of concrete members only marginal, but deformations or cracking indications
are influenced somewhat more.
From the stress-strain behaviour can be deducted:

- lightweight aggregate concrete has a more brittle nature than most dense
  types.

- due to the more triangular shape of the compressed zone, the necessary
  compressed area in the cross-section under review must be larger for a
  given compressive force or moment. This influences the level of the
  neutral axis for elements under bending forces with some benefit to the
  length of eventual flexural cracks.

DESIGN

Weight
Obviously the gain in weight remains an important reason for designs in
lightweight concrete. Spectacular results are achieved in bridge construction. The best known example is the Dyckerhof-bridge at Wiesbaden but also
in Holland the offices appoined to bridge design have designed and executed
a great number of perfect examples like the Tiel-bridge (fig.9). The central part of the bridge is composed of four prestressed precast beams of
65 m long and 3.50 m deep. (aggregate Korlin).
In general savings in own weight do not significantly influence the requi-

red foundations, but these savings are not negligable and a very recent example - still under execution - is a viaduct in a motorway crossing near Haarlem (fig.10). Here the weight advantage is very clear. The foundations are made several years ago according to a scheme based on dense concrete and 2 lane traffic each direction. After the delay, which is normal in road construction (possible not only in Holland), a revised scheme required three lanes each direction. This was met by updating the dense concrete design in a lightweight concept. (aggregate Liapor 6-char.strength 40 N/mm^2). The reduced self weight can also be serious advantageous in erection with prefabricated elements. Crane possibilies are "enlarged" considerably.
In the case of the ABP building at Heerlen (12) the prestressed TT-floor elements for the central span - still weighing some 17 tf - could never have been erected if not executed in lightweight concrete.
As an interesting sideline can be mentioned that the superstructure of this building was originally (1969) fully designed in lightweight concrete. Due to some normal hesitations only the floors were actually executed in light-weight concrete (Korlin aggregate with a characteristic strength of 45 N/mm^2). In a recently erected extension to the building - with a similar structural concept - the attitude has changed to the full lightweight design.

It should be mentioned that research to find optimum combinations of low weight and other properties or characteristics often yields prospective new applications. In this context the research for special (lightweight) mixes for marine-applications should be mentioned (13).

Lightweight concrete mixes with very low densities are developed or in research stadia to reach reduced handling loads and low buoyant weight. The necessary associated low modulus of deformation can be advantageous too.

Special attention should be awarded to the Swedish developed 3L concrete (extremely-light, low absorbent and lightweight). At the FIP-congress in 1978 we were already informed and additional information is given in litt. 9 and 10. Concrete densities in the order of 1200 kg/m^3 are reached with low density aggregates (600-700 kg/m^3), with a reasonable compressive. strength. By adding hydrophobic microparticles to the mix a stable mortar and a waterrepellent concrete does result.

To explain the practical potentials of this very light modification Olav Berge indicates that with the "normal" relation of live loads to own weight in slabs the final deflection for cases with the same live load will be in the same order for dense concrete and for lightweight concretes. This is attributed to the large part of the own weight in the total load and the fact that a lower E modulus not only results in less stiffness in the uncracked stage but also in a greater compressive zone, with a "large" moment of inertia in the cracked stage (9).

Reduced temperature stresses
From design point of view one of the most interesting features of light-weight concrete is its effect on imposed stresses due to temperature changes. These stresses throughout the building are some function of α, E and T $\{\sigma \text{ temp} = f(\alpha, E, T)\}$

The coefficient of lineair expension α-lightweight is about 0,8 α-dense. The E value of lightweight concrete varies, but if we assume E-lightweight = 0,6 E-dense (as a maximum) the effect on temperature stresses is:

σ lightweight = 0.6 x 0.8 σ dense = 0.48 σ dense

Thus imposed temperature stresses are certainly less than 50% of the stres-ses imposed in a dense concrete equivalent case under the same circumstan-

8

ces. This is of coarse valid everywhere, but especially important to structures with exposed concrete facades.
Although the tensile capacity of lightweight concrete itself is mostly less than in a dense case,these temperature stresses are normally covered with reinforcement or prestressing and a substantial saving can be the result of using lightweight concrete.

In the case of fig.11 even the liftshafts are erected in (slipforming) lightweight concrete (12). Main goal was to reduce temperature stresses, because the shafts are partly inside and partly exposed. Additional can be mentioned that none additional cladding was added.
The single wall was sufficient also for thermal insulation.

Fire resistance

The majority of known cases of structural damage to a building is due to fire attach. Much more damage due to fire is reported than for instance due to overloading and in fact even more than all other possible reasons together. So fire has to be accepted as an urgent "loadcase" and use of a material which is better fire resistant can be a design requirement. Concrete has proven to be one of the best structural materials in this respect, but lightweight concrete behaves superior (14,16). Failure in fire (if it ever happens in concrete structures) is mainly due to yield of reinforcement at elevated temperatures.

The most simple reason for better behaviour of the lightweight modifications therefore is the better insulating capacity of the concrete cover to heat transmission. But also the lower thermal expansion and the reduced thermal stresses are reducing the eventual damage to the structure.

A disadvantage can be the high humidity of "young" lightweight concrete. Although this reduces the temperature rise in the reinforcement even more some combinations of aggregate type, high humidity and compressive stress may cause increased spalling in the early months of a building live (mostly in the period of construction) (18). In view of the total lifetime of a building however the risks of damage due to fire are considerably reduced when lightweight concrete is used.

Tensile capacity

In the range of design items that have to be considered especially those related to the tensile capacity are important.
The tensile strength for a dense concrete can be estimated from $fct = k \, fcu^{2/3}$ with $k = 0,25$ according to the Model Code. For lightweight concrete this has to be reduced (fig.7) and the CEB indication for a ratio factor (η_1) is

$0.3 + 0.7 \dfrac{\rho}{2400}$ (5,10), but actual determination must be preferred (fig.1).

Although tensile strength in bending is normally ignored on reinforced concrete calculations we should consider it still influences the design assumptions for shear (and punching shear), torsion, bond and anchorage. Understanding shear phenomena in the bending case has grown slowly over the years. The importance of arch development an tie function of the reinforcement - stipulating the effect of bond - is readily accepted now and for instance clearly outlined in the paper of B.K. Bardhan Roy (15).

The "weaker" response to tensile loadcases stresses the need to carefull detailing. Basically talking about detailing is not restricted to lightweight concrete. On the contrary detailing suited to reinforced concrete is suitable for lightweight aggregate concrete too.

In some cases - like structures executed in lightweight concrete or in the case of fire attack - eventual unsufficient care will possibly be punished earlier. That's why for example in (14) a range of advises about structural detailing are incorporated. Although they are essentially applicable to concrete structures in general, for structures in lightweight concrete it is necessary to comply with them.

For practical purposes fig. 12 (from litt.14) is given, this main idea should be remembered.

Attention should be given to the difference between tensile strength and modulus of rupture values (flexural tensile strength). Modulus of rupture must be regarded as a somewhat fictitions value (18). Extrapolation of its use as commonly advocated in fibre reinforced cementions materials (like G.R.C.) even for cracked, but not yet broken specimens is incorrect.
The assumed stress-strain relation is far from reality.
The design assumptions for phenomena related to tensile capacity should be based upon the determined tensile splitting strength.

Other design principles
Most other design parameters, limit state indications etc., are perfectly dealt with in Bardhan Roy's paper (14). Assuming reinforced concrete as the case with zero prestress they can be applied, thus for the sake of simplicity we refer to that paper.

CONCLUSIONS

Design for lightweight (aggregate) concrete structures will be based on the same principles as design for dense concrete structures. There are no reasons whatsoever to divert from the principle, but for each application the relevant characteristics, of the modification used, have to be known.
Structural behaviour of lightweight concrete is governed by the deformability of the particles or better on the ratio of the stiffnesses of mortar and aggregate. An approach by Grübl to predict or direct the characteristics is given.

The importance sometimes given to the price of a m^3 of concrete is overdue.
The structural advantages to be gained are quite often of much more importance for the structure as whole and can easily lead to lower overal costs of the structure and to better performance.
A range of examples of structures executed in lightweight aggregate concrete is shown in lit. 12, 16 and 17.
Only a few of the profitable characteristics of lightweight concrete, like weight advantages, capacity to reduce imposed temperature stresses and better fire resistance are discussed here. Much more can be taken into account.
It gives however some idea of the approach to use the specific structural behaviour of lightweight concrete.

REFERENCES

1) The many applications of Concrete
   Concrete Construction - Jan. 1980.

2) CEB/FIP Manual of Lightweight Aggregate Concrete
   Design and Technology.
   The Construction Press 1977.

3) The impact of Research on the use of lightweight concrete in major
   structural work.
   J. Bobrowski, P.W. Abeles, B.K. Bardhan Roy.
   Paper to C.I.B. congres Budapest 1974.

4) Why not lightweight Concrete
   J. Bobrowski
   Civil Engineering March 1977.

5) CEB - Model code - chapter 20.

6) Regulations for Concrete (V.B.'74).
   part 6: Lightweight Concrete, additional requirements.
   (Netherlands Standard NEN 3869).

7) Aanvangsspanningen in voorgespannen lichtbeton.
   (Stresses at transfer in prestressed lightweight concrete)
   H. Stoffers
   T.N.O.-report BI-78-42; a concept C.U.R.-report.

8) Biegebemessung von Stahlleichtbeton - Teilbericht zur technologie des
   hochfesten Leichtbeton.
   P. Grübl
   Forchungsreihe der Deutsche Bauindustrie: Band 32.

9) Structures in Lightweight Aggregate Concrete
   Olav Berge. Chalmers Tekniske Högskola publ. 77/2.

10) The Hydrophobe 3L Concrete. A state of the art report.
    Bengt Hedberg, Leif Berntsson, Olav Berge
    Paper to FIP commission on lightweight concrete 1979.

11) FGW - Forschungs vorhaben "Leichtbeton Forschung".
    S. Soretz
    Zement und Beton, heft 2 1976.

12) Emploi des Béton Légers de structures dans la construction des
    Batiments aux Pays-Bas.
    A. Gerritse
    Annales de I.T.B.T.P. - suppl. no. 311 Nov. 1973.

13) Lightweight aggregate concrete for marine structures
    FIP. State of the art report 1978

14) Design and detailing of concrete structures for fire-resistance.
    The Institution of Structural Engineers 1978.

15) Design Considerations for prestressed lightweight aggregate concrete.
    B.K. Bardhan Roy
    Paper to C.I. 80.

16) The structural use of lightweight aggregate concrete.
    B.H. Spratt
    Cement and Concrete Association 1974.

17) Lightweight aggregate Concrete.
    Technology and Word Applications.
    Cem bureau 1974.

18) The spalling of normalweight and lightweight concrete on exposure to
    fire.
    W.J. Copier.
    Heron - 1979 - no. 2.

19) Developments in the measurements of stress/strain behaviour.
    A. Gerritse and A.H. Romijn.
    International G.R.C. Congres London 1979.

Table 1 Indicative values for compressive strength and modulus of deformation of aggregate and cement mortar.

	(Particle) compressive strength	E-value
lightweight agg. cement mortar dense aggregate	$5 - 30$ N/mm^2 $20 - 60$,, $60 - 100$,,	$5 - 30$ kN/mm^2 $20 - 30$,, $60 - 100$,,

Table II Evaluation of formula relating lightweight concrete characteristics to compressive strength by O Berge (9).

Material characteristic	Regression curves	Coefficient of variation δ
Splitting tensile strength f_{ct}	$f_{ct} = (0.12 + 0.88 \frac{\rho}{2400}) f_{cc}^{1/3}$	7.9 %
	$f_{ct} = 0.55 (0.3 + 0.7 \frac{\rho}{2400}) f_{cc}^{1/2}$	9.3 %
	$f_{ct} = 0.42 f_{cc}^{1/2}$	10.6 %
	$f_{ct} = 0.25 f_{cc}^{2/3}$	12.1 %
E-modulus	$E = 3.5 \rho f_{cc}^{1/3}$	10 %
	$E = 1.26 \rho^{3\,2} f_{cc}^{1/2}$	14.5 %
Greep coefficient	$\Phi = \text{constant} \frac{\rho}{f_{cc}^{1/3}}$	17.1 %

Table III Some generalised ratio factors lightweight/dense concrete established in Sweden (10) and partially accepted by CEB.

tensile strength f_{ct}	$0.3 + 0.7 \frac{\rho}{2400}$
creep coefficient ϕ	$0.3 + 0.7 \frac{\rho}{2400}$
shrinkage strain ε_{cs}	$\dfrac{1}{0.3 + 0.7 \frac{\rho}{2400}}$
modulus of deformation	$(\frac{\rho}{2400})^2$

Figure 1 Introductory clauses of Dutch lightweight code.

Clause G.104   **DESIGN**

104.1   In the design of lightweight concrete structures a number of the values expressing the properties of ordinary concrete, as indicated in Chapter A.2, have to be multiplied by ratio factors. A ratio factor indicates the ratio between the values (determined by standard procedures) which respectively characterize the same property of lightweight concrete and ordinary concrete of equal quality. The ratio factors and the maximum strain to be taken into account should be determined by, or under the supervision of, an authorized organization in accordance with the qualification tests indicated in Clause G.609.

104.2   For the type and strength class of the lightweight aggregate to be used, the following values should be determined, by or on behalf of the manufacturer, for the concrete quality (and associated bulk density) which it is proposed to employ:

ν_e = ratio factor for the modulus of elasticity;
ν_k = ratio factor for creep;
ν_r = ratio factor for shrinkage;
ν_f = ratio factor for the tensile strength of the concrete;
$\nu_{f'}$ = ratio factor for the design value of the compressive strength of the concrete;
ϵ'_{ul} = maximum strain to be taken into account in calculations.

The ratio factors for modulus of elasticity, creep, shrinkage and concrete tensile strength should be stated to an accuracy of 0.05, and the ratio factor for the design value of the concrete compressive strength to an accuracy of 0.02. The maximum strain to be taken into account should be accurate to 0.2×10^{-3}.

Figure 2 Indicative interrelation diagram between densities, 28-day cube strength and modulus of deformation according to several literature sources.

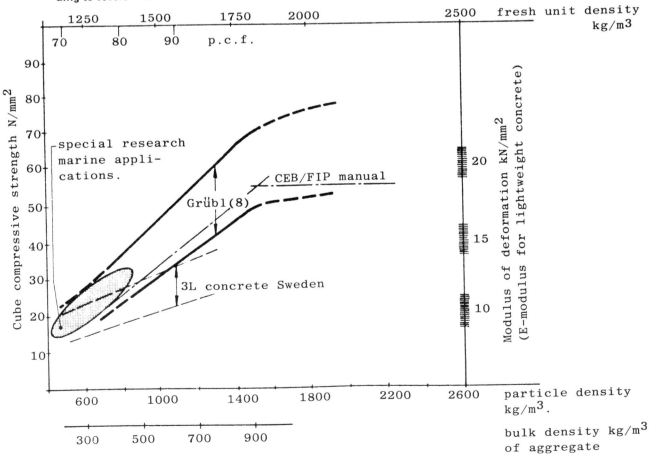

Figure 3 Behaviour of lightweight concrete under compressive force.

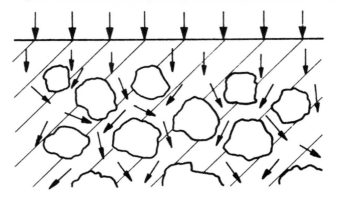

transfer of forces

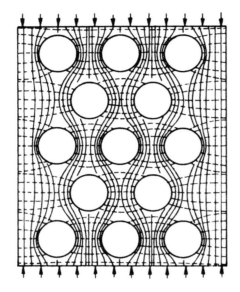

foto elastic determination
of principal stresses

failure pattern

Figure 4 Behaviour of dense concrete under compressive force.

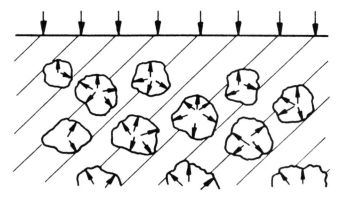

transfer of forces

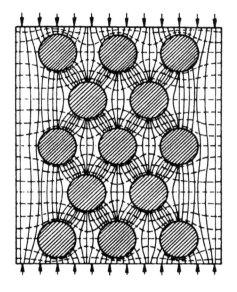

foto elastic determination
of principal stresses

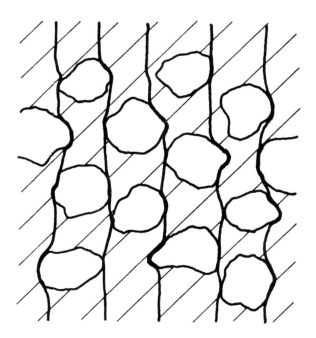

failure pattern

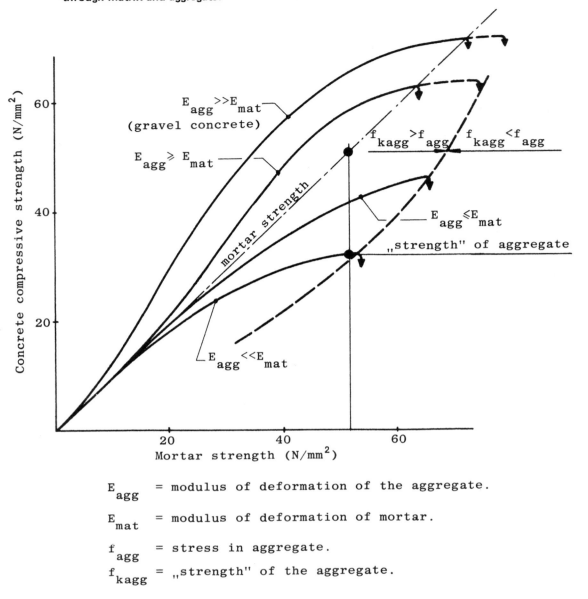

Figure 5 Indicative relation between the strength of concrete, that of mortar and the transfer of forces through matrix and aggregate.

E_{agg} = modulus of deformation of the aggregate.

E_{mat} = modulus of deformation of mortar.

f_{agg} = stress in aggregate.

f_{kagg} = „strength" of the aggregate.

Figure 6 Schematic diagram from literature (8). Strength of lightweight concrete mixes related to comparable mix of same age. Tan a = lightweight concrete aggregate parameter.

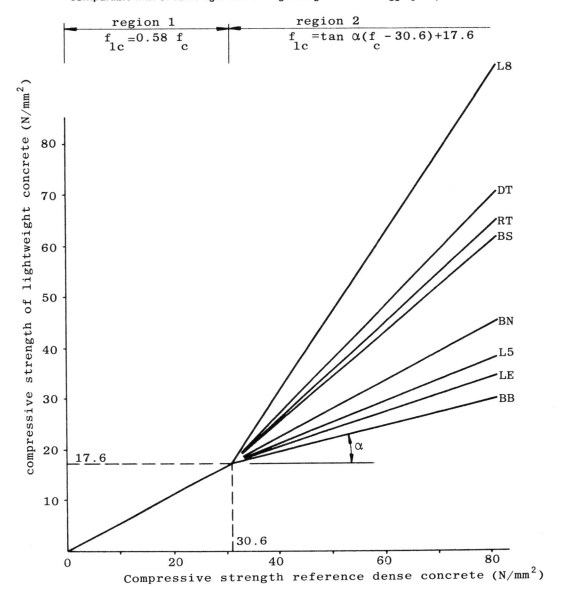

Figure 7   Relation between compressive strength and tensile strength at 28 days. Tests by Grubl (8).

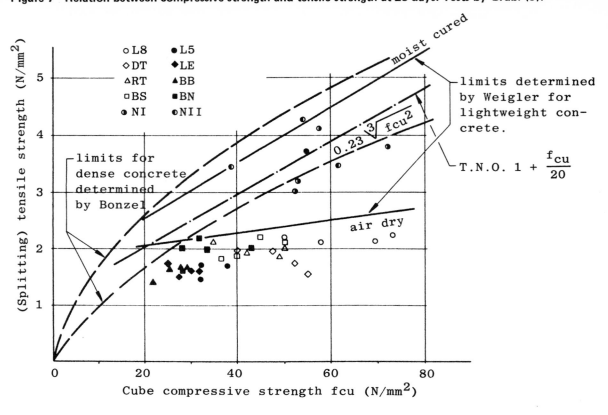

Figure 8   Schematic stress-strain diagrams for concretes with different aggregate stiffness. By Stoffers (7).

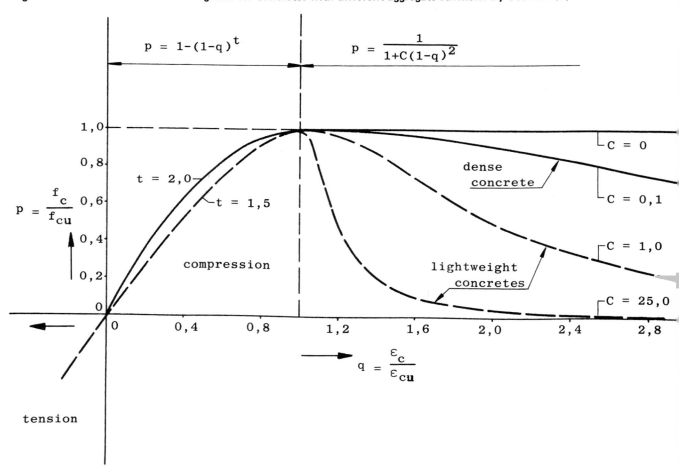

Figure 9 Motorway viaduct, crossing Rottepolderplein.

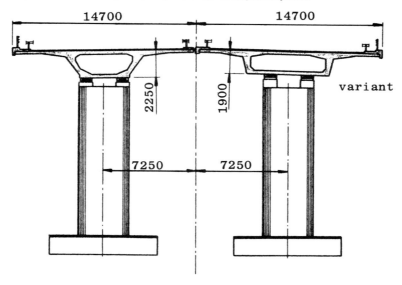

(a) Original scheme in dense concrete

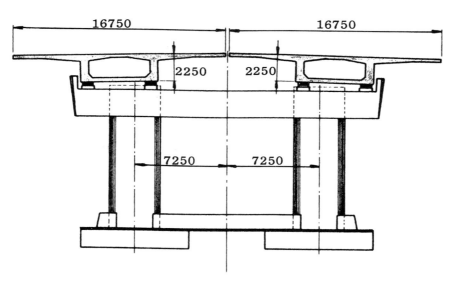

(b) Revised scheme in lightweight aggregate concrete, on existing foundations

Figure 10 Scheme of the Tiel bridge.

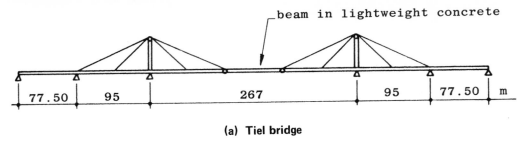

(a) Tiel bridge

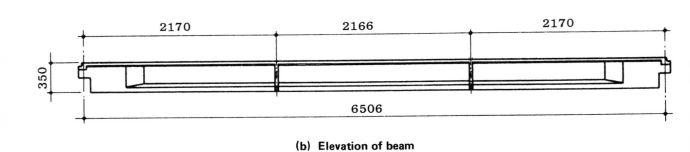

(b) Elevation of beam

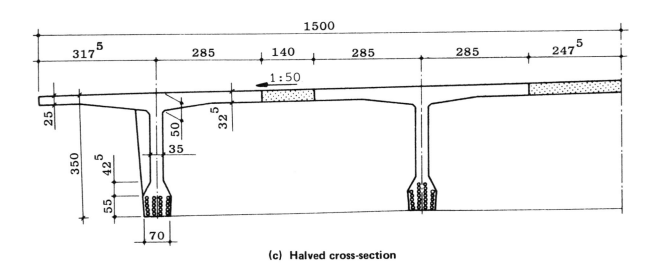

(c) Halved cross-section

Figure 11   WMN-building Utrecht, average floor plan.

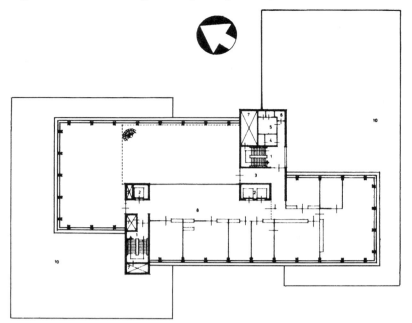

Figure 12 Load transfer before failure of reinforced concrete beams (2, 9, 14).

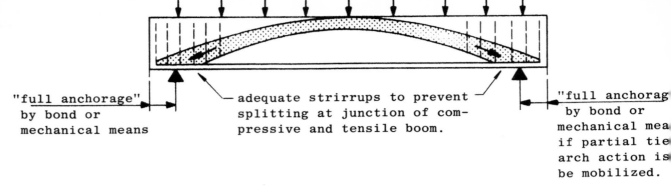

"full anchorage"
by bond or
mechanical means

— adequate strirrups to prevent
splitting at junction of compressive and tensile boom.

"full anchorag
by bond or
mechanical mea
if partial tie
arch action is
be mobilized.

(a) For uniformly distributed load

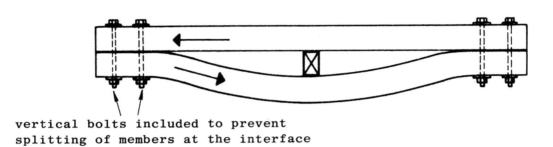

vertical bolts included to prevent
splitting of members at the interface

(b) Bond and anchorage — example analogous to a trussed timber beam

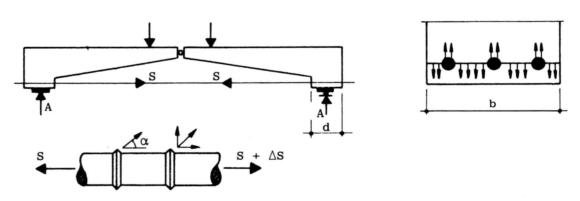

(c) Swedish tests to determine the relationship anchorage/tensile strength of concrete

full anchorage required for
top reinforcement to be
effective at this point.

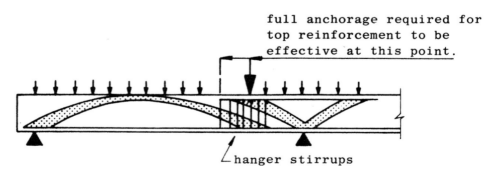

hanger stirrups

(d) Continuous beam

Shear carrying behaviour of lightweight concrete beams as compared to normal weight concrete beams

H R Kirmair
Technical University of Munich, Germany FR

Notations

$\tau_o = \dfrac{Q}{b_o z}$ nominal shear stress

τ design shear stress

Q acting shear force

b_o minimum width of web

z lever arm of internal forces

$\tan\alpha$ inclination of compression struts

w shear crack width

s spacing of stirrups

$\emptyset$ diameter of reinforcing bars

$\sigma_{s\tau}$ stress in stirrups.

This contribution presents a short survey of the research project on the "shear carrying behaviour of lightweight concrete beams with shear reinforcement as compared to nominally identical normal weight concrete beams".

In Germany, the design concept of shear reinforcement distinguishes three ranges as shown in Fig. 1:

range 1) low shear stresses
range 2) medium shear stresses
range 3) high shear stresses

For low shear stresses the reinforcement is calculated on the basis of a truss analogy with an inclination of the compression struts corresponding to $\tan\alpha = 0.4$ for normal weight concrete and $\tan\alpha = 0.5$ for lightweight concrete respectively.

For medium shear stresses $\tan\alpha$ is increased parabolically up to 1.0 corresponding to the MÖRSCH truss model with strut inclination of 45 degrees. For lightweight concrete beams $\tan\alpha$ is 15% larger than for normal weight concrete beams.

For high shear stresses there is no difference in design of the shear reinforcement between lightweight and normal weight concrete. In both cases, design is performed according to a 45 degrees truss model.

Fig. 1 shows the nominal shear stresses for which the design of the test beams has been carried out. To obtain direct comparisons between lightweight and normal weight concrete, the corresponding test beams were designed according to the design rules for normal weight concrete.

Table 1 gives a survey of the test beams. In the range of low shear stresses the cross-section was rectangular. For medium shear stresses a rectangular and a ⊤-beam were tested. In the ⊤-beam the longitudinal reinforcement was staggered. For high shear stresses an ⊥-profile was used. Beams 4 and 5 were made on one half from lightweight concrete and on the other half from normal weight concrete. The reinforcement was identical on both sides. Beams LB I und NB I were also nominally identical. The spacing of the web reinforcement was different on both halves to investigate the influence of stirrup spacing on the shear crack width.

In all beams the web reinforcement consisted of vertical stirrups.

For the longitudinal and transverse reinforcement ribbed steel bars with a nominal yield stress f_y = 420 MN/m^2 and a nominal ultimate strength f_u = 500 MN/m^2 (BSt 420/500 RU according to German Standards) were used.

The lightweight concrete was made of expanded clay aggregate and lightweight sand. It had a specific weight of 1500 kg/m^3. All test beams - normal weight and lightweight concrete - had a concrete cube strength of approximately 35 MN/m^2. The splitting tensile strength was 1.5 to 1.8 MN/m^2 for the lightweight concrete and 2.5 to 3.0 MN/m^2 for the normal weight concrete.

Since the lightweight concrete beam LB II can not directly be compared to a corresponding normal weight concrete beam, the test results are not treated in the following.

Fig. 2 shows the procedure of loading: at first monotonically increasing to the serviceability level, then 50 cycles of loading between serviceability load and 20% of this level, afterwards a 25% overlaod. After unloading, the beams were tested up to failure.

The failure was in each case a flexural one.

The beam designed for high shear stresses was meant to fail by web crushing. Therefore, the beam was designed in bending for a load which was approximately 30% higher than the design load for shear. The failure was still a flexural one but the imminent failure of the web concrete could be seen from the onset of the spalling of the concrete cover. The inclined compressive stresses in the web concrete reached up to 20 MN/m^2, approximately 65 % of the cylinder strength.

The bending failure of the beam designed for medium shear stresses occured near the loading plates simultaneously at the lightweight and normal weight concrete side.

The beam designed for high shear stresses failed in the symmetry axis (Fig. 3).

The cracking at the serviceability level (Fig. 4) showed significant differences between lightweight and normal weight concrete. Due to the lower tensile strength of lightweight concrete, the shear cracking started at lower load levels and the distance between the shear cracks was smaller than in normal weight concrete.

A comparison of the width of the three largest cracks in each beam half is shown in Fig. 5. The columns indicate the crack widths under service loading and the hatched parts the crack widths under 80% of this load, all measured after a preloading of 125% of the service load. The crack widths shown by the hatched columns can in general be regarded to be more relevant with respect to the danger of corrosion of the reinforcement. The maximal permissible crack width can usually be assumed to be 0.3 mm.

The 4 cases shown in Fig. 5 are beam halves designed for low shear stresses with large stirrup spacing of 30 cm, corresponding beam halves with smaller stirrup spacing of 17 cm, beam halves designed for medium and for high stresses respectively.

It can be clearly seen that - in the region of low shear stresses - the shear crack widths of lightweight concrete beams are significantly larger than those of normal weight concrete beams. The shear crack width is in this region highly influenced by the spacing of the stirrups in lightweight concrete. It can be concluded that lightweight concrete beams need special attention with respect to the crack width when they are designed for low shear stresses. Either the stirrup spacing must be limited and/or the amount of shear reinforcement increased.

For medium and high shear stresses no significant difference could be found.

Fig. 6 shows the sum of the shear crack widths of the beams designed for low shear stresses as a function of the load. For the lightweight concrete beam, this sum is larger and significantly effected by the stirrup spacing, while in normal weight concrete the sum of shear crack widths is not influenced by the stirrup spacing.

Fig. 7 presents the maximal stirrup stresses as a function of the applied shear stress. Due to the earlier development of shear cracks in lightweight concrete, the stirrup stresses are higher than in normal weight concrete. The difference is most significant in the range of low shear stresses (beam LB I and NB I) and tends to become smaller as the design shear stress increases. For the beam designed for high shear stresses the difference is approximately 10% approaching the ultimate load.

Summary

The results of the investigations can be summarized as follows:

1) Due to the earlier development of the cracks in lightweight concrete, the stirrup stresses are in general higher

than in nominally identical normal weight concrete beams. The difference becomes smaller as the design shear stress increases.

2) Maximal shear crack widths are larger in lightweight concrete beams designed for low shear stresses, especially in the case of large stirrup spacing. For medium and high shear stresses there is no significant difference.

3) In comparison to normal weight concrete beams, for lightweight concrete beams designed for low shear stresses, a limitation of the stirrup spacing and/or an increase of the shear reinforcement may be necessary.

4) The maximum permissible shear stress specified in the German concrete code provides adequate safety for lightweight concrete beams against failure of the web concrete under inclined compression.

Table 1   Lightweight aggregate producers.

range	beam	cross-section web reinforcement	system	$\tilde{\tau}_0$ MN/m²	tan α
①	LB I	⌀8, s=30; ⌀6, s=17; 4 ⌀22; 22.5; 50	1,65 — 1,65; A — B; 4,30; lightweight concrete	1,0	0,36
	NB I	⌀8, s=30; ⌀6, s=17; 4 ⌀22; 22.5; 50	1,65 — 1,65; 4,30; normal weight concrete	1,0	0,36
②	LB I	⌀12, s=25; ⌀10, s=17; 6 ⌀22; 22.5; 50	1,51 — 1,51; A — B; 4,30; lightweight concrete	1,5	0,63
	IV	⌀10, s=25; 9 ⌀22; 17; 65	3,35 — 3,35; LB — NB; 8,70	1,5	0,61
③	V	⌀12, s=15; 9; 10 ⌀22; 65	2,0 — 2,0; LB — NB; 5,30	4,0	1,0

Figure 1 The relationship between the nominal shear stress and the design shear stress according to DIN 1045.

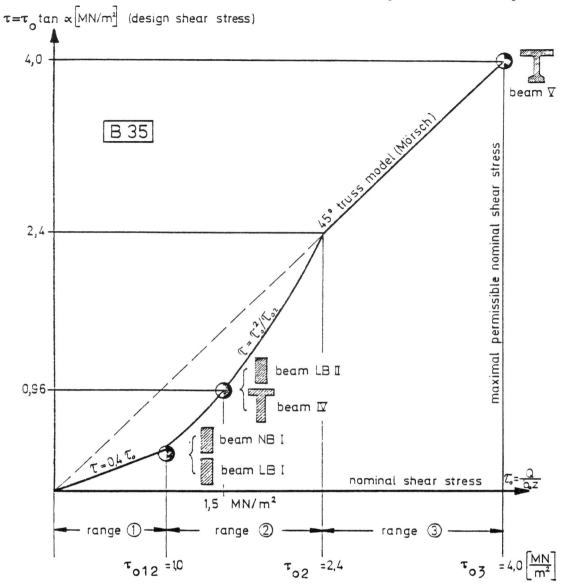

$\tau = \tau_o \tan \alpha \left[MN/m^2\right]$ (design shear stress)

B 35

45° truss model (Mörsch)

maximal permissible nominal shear stress

beam V

$\tau = \tau_o^2/\tau_{o2}$

beam LB II

beam IV

beam NB I

beam LB I

$\tau = 0,4\ \tau_o$

nominal shear stress $\tau_o = \dfrac{Q}{b_0 z}$

1,5 MN/m²

range ① — range ② — range ③

$\tau_{o12} = 1{,}0$ $\tau_{o2} = 2{,}4$ $\tau_{o3} = 4{,}0 \left[\dfrac{MN}{m^2}\right]$

Figure 2 Procedure of loading.

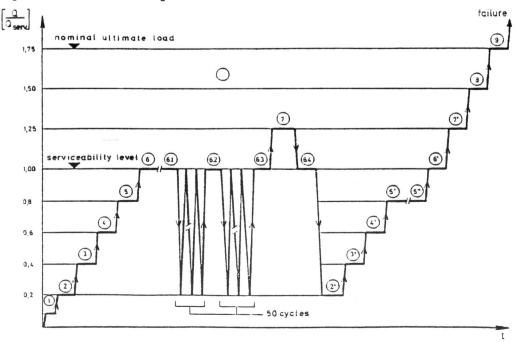

$\left[\dfrac{Q}{Q_{serv}}\right]$

failure

nominal ultimate load

1,75   ⑨

1,50   ⑧

1,25   ⑦   ⑦'

serviceability level ⑥ ⑥.₁ ⑥.₂ ⑥.₃ ⑥.₄   ⑥'

1,00

0,8   ⑤   ⑤' ⑤"

0,6   ④   ④'

0,4   ③   ③'

0,2   ②   ②'

①

— 50 cycles

t

27

Figure 6 Comparison of the sum of the shear crack widths in each half of beam LB I and NB I.

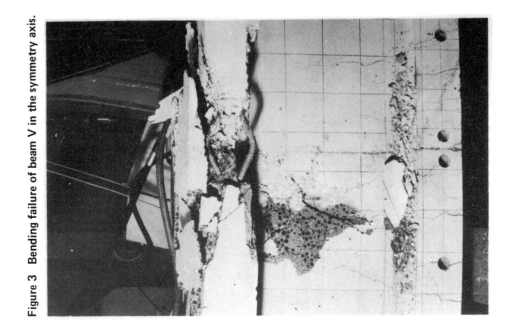

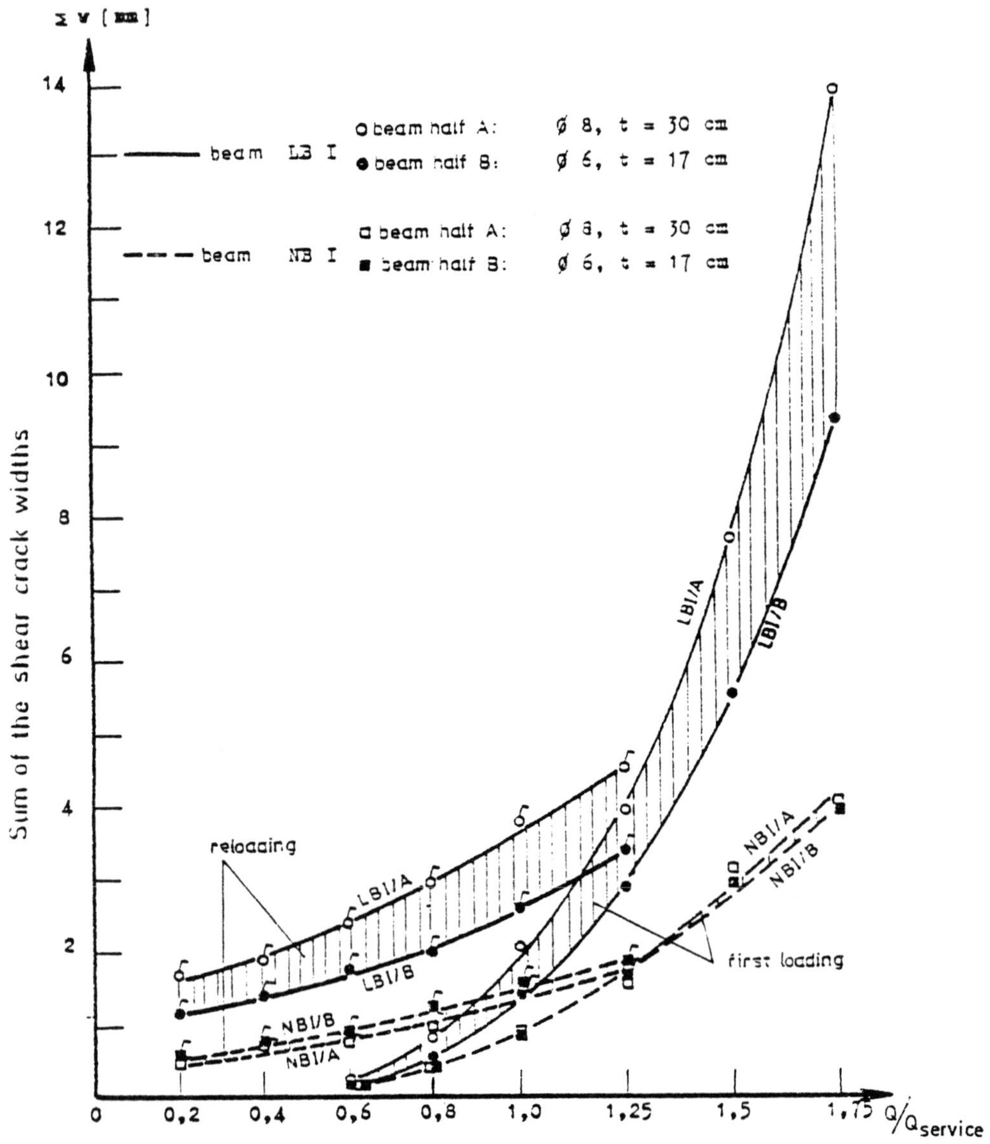

Figure 3 Bending failure of beam V in the symmetry axis.

Figure 4   Crack pattern at the serviceability level.

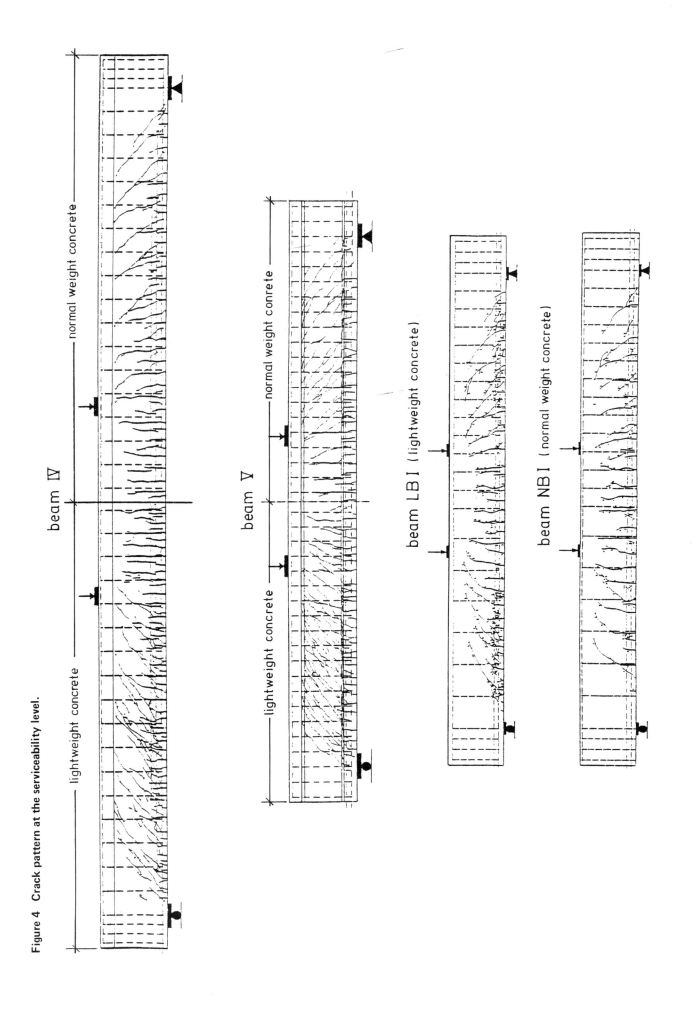

beam Ⅳ

lightweight concrete — normal weight concrete

beam Ⅴ

lightweight concrete — normal weight concrete

beam LBI (lightweight concrete)

beam NBI (normal weight concrete)

29

Figure 5 Comparison of the widths of the three largest shear cracks.

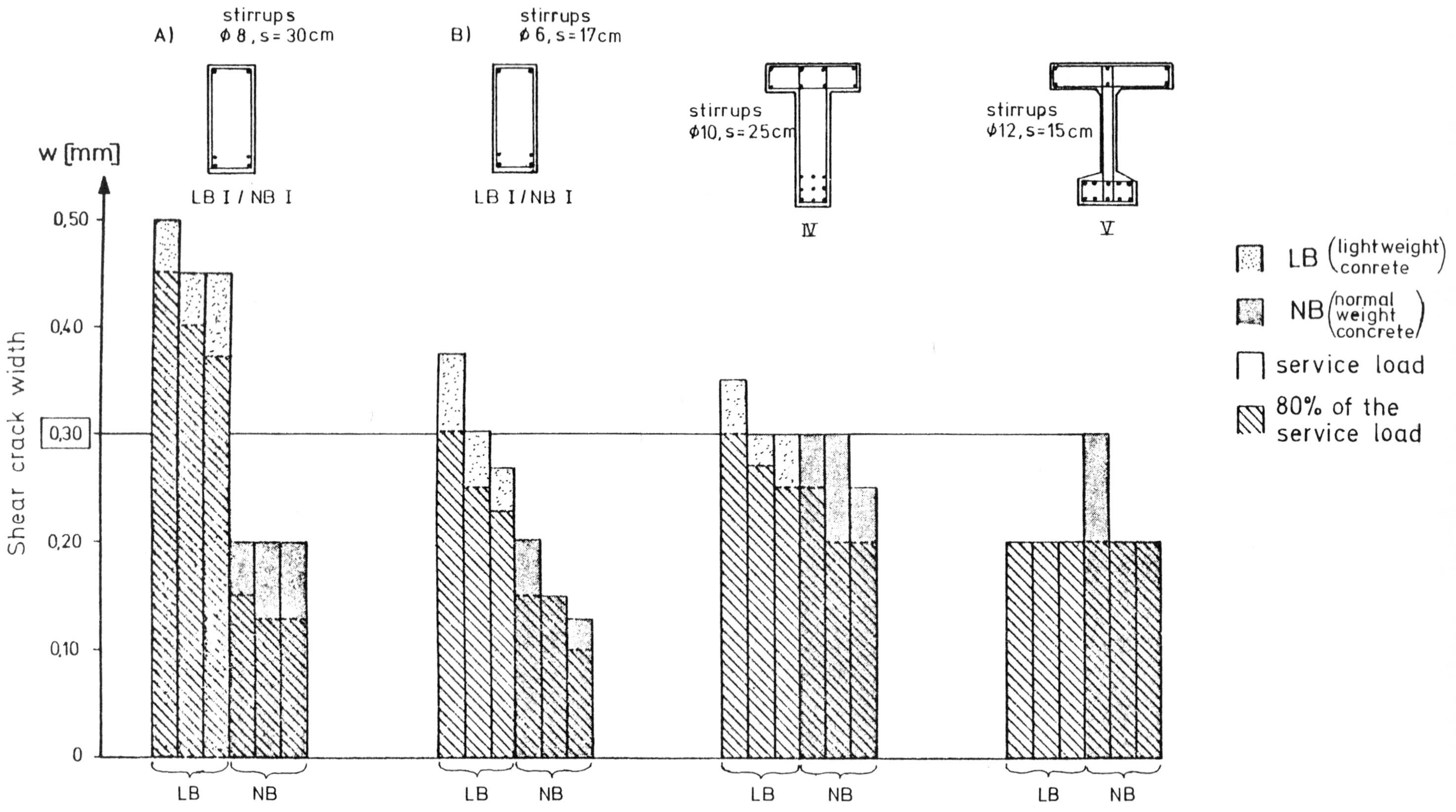

Figure 7 Stirrup stress-load relationship.

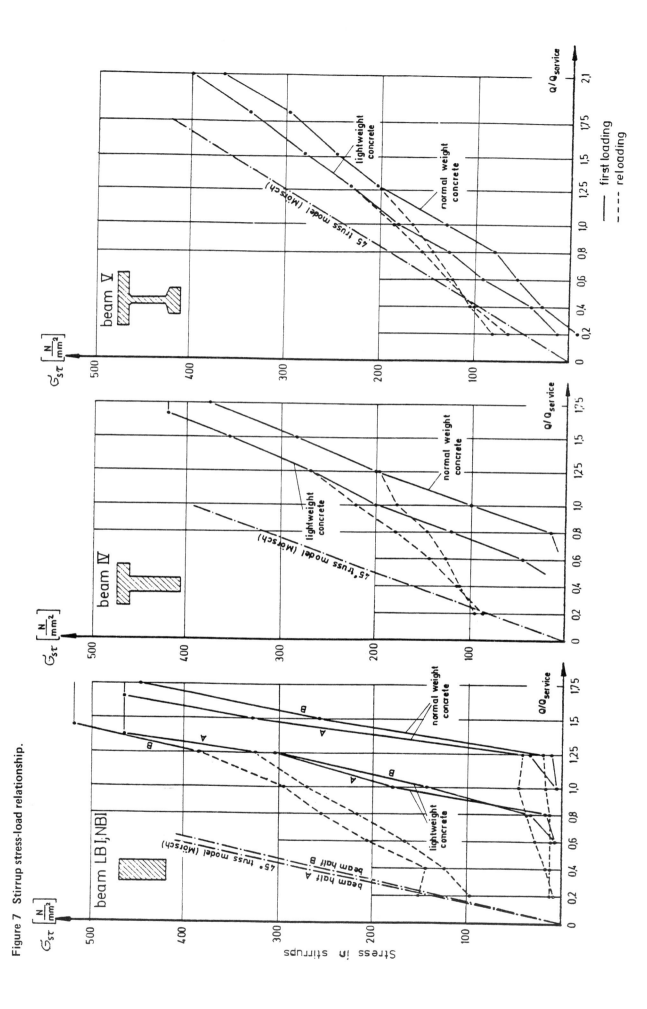

Investigation into sintering coal-mine shales for lightweight aggregate – Part 2

H S Wilson
Canada Centre for Mineral and Energy Technology, Canada

ABSTRACT

Sintering tests were made on two samples of low-carbon coal mine shale from Sydney, N.S. High-carbon shales were blended with them to achieve carbon contents of 2.5 to 9.5%. Physical properties of the lightweight aggregate made from each sinter were determined. The strongest aggregates were produced at carbon contents of 2.5 to 3.5%. Sufficient aggregate was made to prepare two small concrete batches. The air-dry densities of the concretes were 1500 and 1620 kg/m^3 and the 28-d compressive strengths of 76 by 152 mm cylinders were 20.4 and 37.3 MPa. These tests indicate that lightweight aggregate suitable for concrete masonry units could be produced from these shales.

INTRODUCTION

Canadian lightweight aggregate industry

The lightweight aggregate industry in Canada began in 1927 with the processing of shale in a rotary kiln. Divergence of the industry occurred in 1947 when a plant began processing blast furnace slag. During the 1950's and early 1960's, expansion was rapid, production reaching a peak of 730,000 m^3 in 1966. Between 1967 and 1975, production fluctuated between 550 and 660,000 m^3, but by 1978, production from clays, shales and blast furnace slag had decreased to 521,000 m^3, values at $6,892,000 (1).

A total of 16 plants have been built but at present there are 8 in production at 7 locations: 7 processing clay or shale in rotary kilns and one processing blast furnace slag. The producing companies and locations are shown in Table 1.

All but one of the rotary kiln plants use natural gas for fuel, the other using pulverized coal. The heat required in the more efficient plants is about 3.5 Mj/kg of aggregate produced. Production costs have increased for a number of years to a large degree due to the increasing cost of natural gas. In 1979, the cost was 4.4 to 5.4 times its cost in 1973, depending on the area of the country. Because a rotary kiln is only 15% efficient in heat transfer, the cost of fuel is critical to the economics of operation. The lightweight aggregates in Canada must compete with sand, gravel and crushed rock which are produced at lower costs. It is conceivable that some rotary kiln plants may become uneconomic as production costs continue to increase.

Alternate methods of production

The sintering method of producing lightweight aggregate makes more efficient use of the fuel in that the fuel is intimately mixed with the raw material. This method of production has not been used in Canada, but it has been used successfully both in Europe and in the United States, using surface shales and clays as raw materials. A fuel must be added to these materials to furnish the heat required for sintering (2). Fly ashes have also been sintered successfully for a number of years in Europe and also with some success in the United States. These materials contain carbon and some times can be sintered with no addition or only slight adjustment of the carbon content.

Shales associated with coal deposits are another type of raw material which has been used in Europe for a number of years. The shale is of necessity, mined with the coal and is separated from it in washing plants. The shale, which is a reject material, contains carbon as a constituent and also contains coal, the proportion of coal depending on the washing process.

OBJECTIVE OF STUDY

An extensive study has been undertaken by CANMET to determine if the coal mine shales in Canada are potential raw materials, using an alternate process to the current rotary kiln process. Materials are being collected from selected coal washery plants in different areas of the country and are to be assessed by the sintering method of production. The proposed application of the lightweight aggregates is in concrete masonry units. Over 70% of the current production of lightweight aggregates is in this application.

POTENTIAL SOURCES OF RAW MATERIALS

High- and medium-volatile bituminous coals are mined in Nova Scotia and New Brunswick. Sub-bituminous and low- and medium-volatile bituminous coals are mined in Alberta. Low- and medium-volatile coals are also mined in British Columbia, and lignite coal is mined in Saskatchewan (3).

LABORATORY INVESTIGATION

PHASE I

Raw materials

Shales from Sydney, Nova Scotia were selected for this phase of the study. The coarse coal washery reject from the Victoria Junction preparation plant of Cape Breton Development Corporation (VJC-1), the principal raw material, was received in the laboratory in December, 1978. The analysis is shown in Table 2.

This shale contains unsufficient fuel for sintering, and the coal-washery reject from the Prince mine (P) was selected as the fuel to be used as an additive to the Victoria Junction shale. The proximate analysis of the Prince shale is shown in Table 3.

X-ray diffraction analyses (XRD) of the two shales were made in a Guinier-deWolff quadruple focussing camera. Estimates of the approximate proportions of the minerals identified were made by visual comparison of the intensities of selected diffraction lines. The results are as follows:

VJC-1: quartz (40%), mica (25%), kaolin (15%), pyrite (10%), siderite (10%), remainder: chlorite (?), K-feldspar (?).

P: quartz (25%), mica (25%), pyrite (25%), kaolin (25%), remainder: feldspar (trace).

Differential thermal analyses (DTA) of the two shales showed carbon, clay minerals, pyrite and quartz, but did not give much information on the relative proportions. Reactions were overshadowed and perhaps hidden by the extremely strong exothermic carbon reaction.

The Victoria Junction shale, which was minus 50 mm as received, was crushed to minus 9.5 mm, and the Prince shale was crushed to minus 2.36 mm.

Sintering tests

The two shales were blended in proportions to result in various fixed carbon contents, the blending being done dry in a small drum concrete mixer from which the paddles had been removed. The blend was then pelletized (or agglomerated) in the same concrete mixer, water being added from a spray gun. The pelletizing conditions approximated those in a pelletizing disc, except that the raw material and water were not added continuously as in the disc, but alternately and in small increments. Each batch for sintering totaled 7.3 kg of dry material. The sintering equipment is shown in Fig. 1.

The pelletized batch was placed in the sintering pot without compaction, level with the top of the pot, which was 215 mm diameter at the bottom, 240 mm diameter at the top, and 150 mm deep ($0.02m^3$). Material not used to charge the pot was dried and the grading determined using sieves: 4, 6, 8, 10 and 20 mesh (4.75, 3.35, 2.36, 2.00 mm and 850 μm). A Fineness Modulus was calculated on the plus 850 μm material to determine the relative size ranges of the various pelletized charges. Screening was done on hand sieves, gently and for a short time to reduce break-down of pellets.

The surface of the charge was heated by the gas-fired ignition hood at a draft of 25 mm water gauge. When the surface of the charge had reached sufficient temperature to support combustion of the fuel, the hood was turned off and the draft was increased to the desired pressure. The induced draft was measured by a manometer connected to the exhaust flue. The flue passed through a cold water heat exchanger to condense the volatiles in the exhaust gases before they reached the fan. Unshielded thermocouples in the pot and in the plenum below the pot were used to measure the temperature of a point in the charge near the grate and of the exhaust gases. The test was continued until it was considered that sintering was complete. Fig. 2 illustrates the structure of a typical sinter. Thirteen tests were made, blending the shales to give carbon contents of 7, 5.5, 3.5 and 2.5%, and varying the conditions of the charge and of the sintering draft. The conditions of each test are shown in Table 4.

The sinter was broken into pieces, the minus 19 mm and unsintered materials were discarded after being weighed, and recovery was recorded as the plus 19 mm sinter. This material was crushed, screened and recombined to have the following grading:

$$9.5 \text{ to } 4.75 \text{ mm} = 75\%$$
$$4.75 \text{ to } 2.36 \text{ mm} = 25\%$$

This graded lightweight aggregate was used to determine the dry, loose unit weight and the crushing strength. The unit weight was determined using a cylindrical metal container of 0.9×10^{-3} m^3. The crushing strength measurement is not a standard test in North America but is similar to British standard B.S. 812:1967 - Method for the Sampling and Testing of Mineral Aggregates, Sands and Fillers. In the tests done at CANMET, the graded aggregate is placed without compaction in a 75-mm diameter steel cylinder to a depth of 125 mm. A steel plunger compacted the aggregate 25 mm and a total of 50 mm using a hydraulic press. The pressures required to give these two degrees of compaction are reported as the crushing strength. The physical properties of the lightweight aggregates are shown in Table 5.

PHASE 2

To obtain information on concrete that could be made with lightweight aggregate made from these shales, four sinter tests were made. Four batches, blends of VJC-1 and P, each containing 3.5% carbon, were pelletized, using similar conditions, and the four products mixed. Four sintering tests were made, again attempting to have similar conditions which are shown in Table 4. The sinters were crushed, blended into one large batch and the unit weight and crushing strength were determined, those results being shown in Table 5.

The aggregate was subsequently graded within the limits specified in ASTM C331-77: Lightweight Aggregates for Concrete Masonry Units (4). The grading and ASTM limits are shown in Table 6 and graphically in Fig. 3. The dry, loose unit weight, the saturated surface-dry (SSD) specific gravity and the 24-h absorption were determined and are shown in Table 6.

Two small concrete batches were proportioned, using the aggregate graded as described above, and cement contents were expected to give medium- and high-strength concretes. The aggregate was presoaked for 24 h with 18% water to satisfy the absorption. Each batch was $0.004m^3$, mixing being done in a slow-speed, Hobart impeller mixer. From each batch, four 76 by 152 mm cylinders were made, the two layers of concrete in each cylinder were consolidated by external vibration.

The specimens were removed from the moulds after 24 h, weighed in air and suspended in water to determine the density and stored in a moist-curing room at $23.1 \pm 1.7°C$ and 100% relative humidity for 6 days. They were then placed in a dry-curing room at $23 \pm 1.1°C$ and a relative humidity of $50 \pm 5\%$ until tested at 28 d. Prior to testing, they were weighed and capped then broken in compression.

The mix proportions and the properties of the hardened concretes are shown in Table 7. Typical fracture surfaces of the cylinders are illustrated in Fig. 4.

PHASE 3

Raw materials

There was not enough of the VJC-1 shale to do further testing and a second shipment of coarse washery rejects from the Victoria Junction plant (VJC-2) was received December, 1979. The analysis of this shale is shown in Table 8.

This shipment of shale contained considerably more carbon than the first. Although it was considered that it might sinter satisfactorily without addition of a fuel, a shipment of fine rejects from the Victoria Junction plant (VJ-F) was selected as additive for some of the tests. The proximate analysis of this shale is shown in Table 9.

X-ray diffraction analysis of these two shales, gave the following estimated approximate proportions:

VJC-2: quartz (30%), mica (25%), siderite (15%), pyrite (15%), kaolin (15%), remainder: chlorite (?), K-feldspar (?).

VJ-F: quartz (25%), mica (25%), pyrite (20%), kaolin (15%), gypsum (15%), remainder: jarosite, siderite, chlorite (?) K-feldspar.

Differential thermal analyses on these two shales showed that the coarse VJC-2 shale contained carbon, clay minerals and pyrite and the VJ-F shale contained carbon, clay minerals, pyrite and gypsum. As with the analyses of VJC-1 and P shales, the reactions were overshadowed by the carbon reaction.

Sintering tests

For sintering tests the VJC-2 shale was crushed to minus 4.75 mm and the VJ-F shale was crushed to minus 2.36 mm. Nine sinter tests were made, the first three blending the VJC-2 and the VJ-F to have carbon contents of 9.5, 6.8 and 5.1%. Blending was done dry in the Hobart mixer used in mixing the concrete in Phase 2; the blending time was 15 minutes. Five tests were made with the VJC-2 shale alone, the carbon content of each batch being 3.3%. One test was made using a batch of 13.6 kg of dry VJC-2 shale. A 100 mm extension was added to the sintering pot giving a total depth to the charge of 250 mm.

The pelletizing and sintering procedures, and the evaluation of the sintered products were the same as those reported in Phase I of this report. The pelletizing and sintering conditions are shown in Table 10. The dry, loose unit weights and crushing strengths of each of the aggregates are shown in Table 11.

DISCUSSION OF RESULTS

Satisfactory sintering was accomplished at all carbon contents between 7.0 and 2.5% in Phase I and between 9.5 and 3.5 in Phase 3. The highest crushing strengths were achieved from the sinters with the lowest carbon content. This increase was at the expense of recovery, which would be expected considering the small volume of the pot. The crushing of the VJC-2 finer than VJC-1 resulted in smaller pellets as indicated by lower FM values in Phase 3 than in Phase 1. This finer grading seems to have reduced the recovery about 10%. Considering the number of tests that can be compared, the draft does not seem to have had a great effect on the recovery or the crushing strength. Sinters 24 and 25, with moisture contents of only 4.8 and 5.2%, gave aggregates of higher crushing strength than did comparable sinters with higher moisture content. Davies and Mitchell (5) showed how increasing moisture content resulted in a more abrupt increase in temperature of a point within a sinter bed. This indicates that a slower increase in temperature is more advantageous to strength development.

The standard concrete specimen used in North America for compressive strength determinations is a 152 by 305 mm cylinder. On the basis of data published by the U.S. Bureau of Reclamation and by Malhotra, the compressive strength of a 76 by 152 mm cylinder is in the order of 20% higher than that of a 152 by 305 mm cylinder (6,7). A factor of 0.8 applied to the strengths of the 76 by 152 mm cylinders gives strengths of mixes 1 and 2 of 16.3 and 29.8 MPa, respectively. These strengths are considered adequate for medium- and high-strength concrete masonry. The unit weights are also within acceptable limits.

A problem which can be encountered with a raw material such as this is variation in composition. The Cape Breton Development Corp. supplied ash analyses taken at 8 periods between September 28, 1978 and November 3, 1979. Table 10 shows the variation in composition during that period. As can be seen, the variation was not great during that period, and other than the carbon, the shale could be considered constant in composition. The carbon content is of great importance. On the basis of the heating value, the carbon apparently varied from less than 1% to about 4%.

The sulphur content of VJC-2 was 2.3%. During sintering the sulphur probably would all be converted to sulphur dioxide (SO_2). This percentage of sulphur is apparently marginal in acceptability in the Cape Breton area of Nova Scotia. An extension to this study is being undertaken to determine if limestone ($CaCO_3$) is effective in convering SO_2 to calcium sulphate ($CaSO_4$) which would be retained in the sinter bed. Even if it is partly effective it would probably reduce the SO_2 content of the exhaust gases below the minimum level of acceptability.

CONCLUSIONS

The tests reported here indicate that a lightweight aggregate can be made from a coal mine shale, a reject from the Victoria Junction preparation plant of Cape Breton Development Corp., Sydney, N.S. The dry, loose unit weight was well below the maximum specified by ASTM. The aggregate with the highest crushing strength was produced from shale or blend of shales containing 2.5 to 3.5% fixed carbon. Limited testing in concrete using 76 by 152 mm cylinders gave air dry densities from 1700 to 1750 kg/m^3 and 28-d compressive strengths from 20.4 to 37.3 MPa. These properties indicate that a lightweight aggregate such as this could be used in lightweight concrete masonary units.

REFERENCES

1. Stonehouse, D.H. "Lightweight aggregates"; Can Minerals Yearbook; Energy, Mines and Resources Canada; 1978.

2. Wilson, H.S. "Lightweight aggregates: properties, applications and outlook"; CANMET Report 79-33; CANMET, Energy, Mines and Resources, Canada; 1979.

3. Aylsworth, J.A. and Weyland, H.J. "Coal and coke"; Can Minerals Yearbook; Energy, Mines and Resources Canada; 1977.

4. "Lightweight aggregates for concrete masonry units"; ASTM Specification C331-77; Annual Book of ASTM Standards; Part 14, 231-233; 1979.

5. Davies, W. and Mitchell, D.W. "Developments in sintering efficiency"; Proc Int Min Dressing Cong; 305-364; 1957.

6. "Concrete Manual", U.S. Bureau of Reclamation; 7th edition: 582; 1963.

7. Malhotra, V.M.   "Are 4 x 8-inch concrete cylinders as good as 6 x 12-inch cylinders for quality control of concrete?"; Lab Report 73-35 (IR); Mines Branch (since renamed CANMET) Energy, Mines and Resources Canada; 1972.

Table 1   Lightweight aggregate producers.

Company	Location	Raw material
Aerlite Products Ltd.	Edmonton, Alberta	clay
Avon Aggregates Ltd.	Minto, New Brunswick	shale
Cindercrete Products Ltd.	Regina, Saskatchewan	clay
Domtar Inc.	Mississauga, Ontario	shale
Genstar Ltd.	Calgary, Alberta	shale
Genstar Ltd. (Edcon Block Div.)	Edmonton, Alberta	clay
Kildonan Concrete Products Ltd.	St. Boniface, Manitoba	clay
National Slag Ltd.	Hamilton, Ontario	blast furnace slag

Table 2   Analysis of coarse Victoria Junction shale, VJC-1: 1978.

Ash analysis %*		Proximate analyses %**	
SiO_2	58.64		
Al_2O_3	21.67	Moisture	0.73
Fe_2O_3	11.21	Ash	89.36
TiO_2	0.49	Volatile	9.28
P_2O_5	0.20	Fixed carbon	0.63
CaO	0.59	Gross kj/kg	1200*
MgO	2.00		
Na_2O	0.46		
K_2O	4.52		
SO_3	0.10		
	99.88		

**Supplied by Cape Breton Development Corp.

**Determined by CANMET

Table 3   Proximate analysis of Prince shale (P).*

Moisture	2.23
Ash	51.03
Volatile	21.10
Fixed carbon	25.64

*Determined at CANMET

Table 4 Pelletizing and sintering conditions – phases 1 and 2.

Sinter No.	Proportion of raw materials	Carbon, %	Water added %	Ignition time, sec	draft mm	time min	Sinter charge kg	recovery %	FM raw pellets	Remarks
1	67% VJC-1 33% P	7	8.4	60	200–300	60	6.6	66	3.0	Sintered almost to grate in centre
2	67% VJC-1 33% P	7	–	50	100	80	7.5	62	–	Sintered to grate
3	67% VJC-1 33% P	7	7.7	30	100–150	57	6.3	76	3.1	Sintered almost to grate in centre
4	75% VJC-1 25% P	5.5	7.4	90	200–300	55	7.3	63	2.5	Ignited twice – 60 and 30 sec Sinter not complete in centre
5	75% VJC-1 25% P	5.5	–	60	150–25	61	7.4	57	–	Sinter not complete in centre
6	75% VJC-1 25% P	5.5	7.8	30	150–50	68	6.8	74	2.5	Sintered to grate
7	75% VJC-1 25% P	5.5	10.4	30	150–50	27	6.7	42	4.1	35 mm channel down centre not sintered
8	75% VJC-1 25% P	5.5	9.4	30	100–75	53	6.6	57	3.7	Top of sinter irregular Sinter not complete in centre
9	85% VJC-1 15% P	3.5	7.0	60	100–50	48	6.8	53	3.5	Ignited twice – 30 and 40 sec. Top of sinter irregular. Sinter not complete in centre
10	85% VJC-1 15% P	3.5	7.2	45	100	48	6.9	58	3.5	Sintered almost to grate in centre
11	85% VJC-1 15% P	3.5	8.5	40	100	48	6.7	50	3.7	Sintered almost to grate in centre
12	90% VJC-1 10% P	2.5	7.3	60	100–50	45	7.1	35	3.4	Top of sinter irregular Sintered to grate
13	90% VJC-1 10% P	2.5	7.0	65	50	55	7.2	45	3.6	Sintered almost to grate in centre
14	85% VJC-1 15% P	3.5	7.3	30	100	51	–	53	2.7	Sintered almost to grate in centre
15	85% VJC-1 15% P	3.5	7.3	30	100	63	–	48	2.7	Sintered to grate
16	85% VJC-1 15% P	3.5	7.3	40	100	60	–	45		Sintered almost to grate in centre
17	85% VJC-1 15% P	3.5	7.3	40	100	63	–	56		Sintered almost to grate in centre

Table 5 Physical properties of aggregates — phases 1 and 2.

Sinter No.	Unit weight kg/m^3	Crushing strength, MPa	
		25 mm	50 mm
1	563.9	1.4	5.4
2	612.0	1.7	6.8
3	547.9	1.4	5.1
4	624.8	1.8	7.5
5	639.2	1.9	7.6
6	570.3	1.7	5.7
7	581.5	1.8	6.4
8	583.1	2.4	7.7
9	600.8	2.3	8.7
10	608.8	3.0	10.3
11	612.0	2.8	10.2
12	663.2	2.7	11.7
13	647.2	2.6	11.6
14			
15	658.4	3.0	11.1
16			
17			
ASTM maximum	880	–	–

Table 6 Grading and properties of lightweight aggregate.

Sieve size	Cumulative % passing	
	Aggregate	ASTM limits
9.5 mm	100	90–100
4.75 mm	75	65–90
2.36 mm	50	35–65
1.40 mm	40	–
600 μm	28	–
300 μm	18	10–25
150 μm	12	5–15

Dry, loose unit weight: 849.1 kg/m^3

SSD bulk specific gravity: 1.73

24-h absorption: 17.8%

Table 7 Mix proportions and properties of hardened concrete.

Mix No.	Cement kg/m³	Water kg/m³	Aggregate SSD kg/m³	Water-cement ratio*	Aggregate-cement ratio*	Hardened concrete		
						Density kg/m³ 1-d	28-d	Compressive strength 28-day MPa
1	313	166	1194	0.53	3.81	1703	1506	20.4
2	430	167	1136	0.39	2.64	1751	1621	37.3

*by weight

Table 8 Analysis of coarse Victoria Junction shale, VJC-2: 1979.

Ash analysis, %*		Proximate analysis, %**	
SiO_2	58.70	Moisture	0.75
Al_2O_3	22.41	Ash	86.16
Fe_2O_3	8.80	Volatile	9.80
TiO_2	0.50	Fixed carbon	3.29
P_2O_5	0.20	Sulphur	2.31
CaO	0.74	Gross kj/kg	2062*
MgO	1.83		
Na_2O	0.85		
K_2O	3.81		
SO_3	0.41		
	98.25		

*Supplied by Cape Breton Development Corp.

**Determined by CANMET

Table 9 Proximate analysis of fine Victoria Junction shale, VJ-F.*

Moisture	2.00
Ash	59.22
Volatile	17.78
Fixed carbon	21.00
Sulphur	2.33

*Determined at CANMET

Table 10 Pelletizing and sintering conditions — phase 3.

Sinter No.	Proportion of raw materials	Carbon %	Water added %	Ignition time sec	draft mm	Sinter time min	Sinter charge kg	recovery %	FM raw pellets	Remarks
18	65% VJC-2 35% VJ-F	9.5	9.4	30	100–150	65	6.5	77	2.5	Sintered to grate
19	80% VJC-2 20% VJ-F	6.8	9.1	35	100–200	80	6.9	72	2.4	Sintered to grate
20	90% VJC-2 10% VJ-F	5.1	8.9	45	100–200	60	7.0	58	2.5	35 mm channel through charge not sintered
21	100% VJC-2	3.3	7.3	40	100	42	7.3	37	2.8	35 mm channel through charge not sintered
22	100% VJC-2	3.3	–	90	100	52	–	46	2.6	Ignited twice – 60 and 30 sec. Sintered to grate, some on top not sintered
23	100% VJC-2	3.3	6.1	60	150–300	39	7.1	35	2.8	Top of sinter very irregular Sintered to grate
24	100% VJC-2	3.3	4.8	90	150–250	36	7.6	37	2.8	25 mm channel through charge not sintered. Sintered to grate
25	100% VJC-2	3.2	5.3	85	100–200	60	7.3	43	2.7	Sintered to grate
26	100% VJC-2	3.3	6.3	150	150–200	97	13.5	44	3.0	Ignited 4 times 45, 30, 30 and 45 sec. Top 25–35 mm not sintered. Sintered to grate

Table 11 Physical properties of aggregates — phase 3.

Sinter No.	Unit weight kg/m³	Crushing strength, MPa	
		25 mm	50 mm
18	495.0	1.4	4.5
19	552.3	1.6	6.1
20	552.7	2.0	7.2
21	591.1	2.4	9.5
22	595.9	2.1	9.0
23	594.3	2.6	10.4
24	602.4	3.0	12.7
25	592.7	2.8	12.0
26	647.2	3.2	12.4
ASTM maximum	880	-	-

Table 12 Range in analysis of Victoria Junction shale.*

Ash analysis, %	
SiO_2	57.22–58.90
Al_2O_3	21.08–22.53
Fe_2O_3	8.80–11.21
TiO_2	0.49– 0.70
P_2O_5	0.13– 0.52
CaO	0.27– 0.74
MgO	1.56– 2.11
Na_2O	0.40– 1.04
K_2O	3.56– 4.52
SO_3	0.10– 3.07
Gross kj/kg	2062–2308

*Supplied by Cape Breton Development Corp.

Figure 1 Sintering equipment.

A. Ignition hood
B. Sintering pot
C. Extension ring
D. Plenum
E. Exhaust flue

F. Heat exchanger
G. Exhaust fan
H. Exhaust stack
I. Temperature recorder

45

Figure 2 Structure of typical sinter.

5 mm

5 mm

Figure 3   Grading of lightweight aggregate.

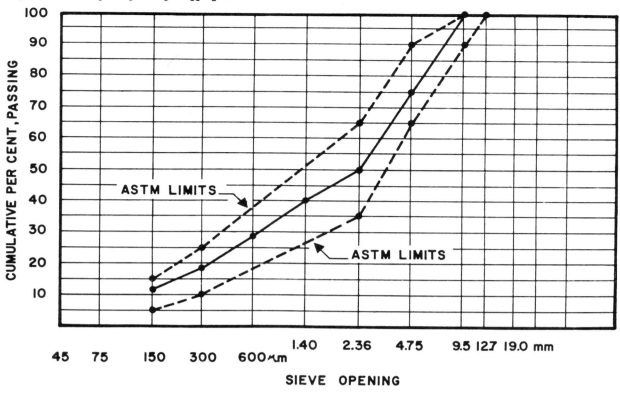

Figure 4   Fracture surfaces of cylinders.

Author's introduction to 'Properties of hardened lightweight aggregate concrete'

F D Lydon
The University of Wales Institute of Science and Technology, UK

It may be interesting to note that, whereas Figure 1 refers to Lytag coarse aggregates and natural sand, previous work[64] has indicated that where Lytag fine aggregate is used instead of natural sand, the relation between 28-day cube strength and cement content for medium workability, corresponds closely with that for high workability in Figure 1 up to a cement content of about 550 kg/m^3; thereafter it approaches the curve for medium workability Lytag/sand concrete.

The paper indicates that with reference to stress/strain behaviour in uniaxial compression most researchers have concluded that lightweight aggregate concretes are rather more brittle than normal 'dense' concretes. However a most important note is included in the last paragraph of the section 'Short-term stress/strain behaviour' which emphasises that the work referred to deals with plain concrete and that the presence of transverse reinforcement renders the material ductile. It must be realised that any experienced designer will ensure that ductile behaviour will be the norm for reinforced elements and that it is the behaviour of the composite material which, in practice, is important.

Under the section 'Tensile strain capacity' some experimental results are included (shown in Figure 5) which indicate rather better behaviour by Lytag (coarse and fine aggregates) concrete compared with crushed limestone coarse aggregates and marine sand concrete. It should be noted that the uniaxial tensile stress, here, is f_{dc}, i.e. the stress at the onset of stable fracture propagation and not the tensile strength. It has been suggested [15] that there may be a useful correlation between uniaxial tensile strain capacity and uniaxial tensile strength.

Accordingly data for the 100 and 75 percent relative humidity curing from Figure 5 are combined with data from Reference 15 to produce Figure 8. All test specimens from the latter were cured under water until tested. It is seen that both sets of data complement each other well and, considering the nature of the experimental measurements, there is a high degree of correlation between the tensile strain capacity and the tensile strength.

It is noted, in the last paragraph under 'Creep and shrinkage', that restricted drying of laboratory specimens of lightweight concrete has resulted in expansion with moisture loss. Figure 9 is an updated version of that given in reference 52. The influence of partial sealing (which allowed some moisture loss) on the volume change is evident, as is the removal of the sealing on the drying shrinkage. It is not suggested that the actual values shown are typical; they will obviously be affected by the type of concrete, its conditioning and the sealing system. But the principle may have practical consequences for full-scale structures or structural elements.

A cautionary note is sounded in paragraph three of the section 'Absorption and permeability' referring to the rates of surface absorption through good quality, mature, lightweight aggregate concrete. This is based on some experimental work on a set of cubes (101.6 mm) of coarse and fine Lytag aggregate concrete which had been cured in water for nine years. Some tests were also conducted on mature 'normal' aggregate concrete, for comparison. Results are shown in Figure 10. Limits which have been suggested [60] for the 10 minute and 60 minute initial surface absorption values appropriate to reinforced and prestressed concrete are shown and it is clear that whereas the mature high strength 'normal' concrete falls well below them the corresponding lightweight concrete values significantly exceed them. This cannot be because the 'quality' of this concrete is inferior and therefore considerable care should be exercised in applying inappropriate criteria to the lightweight material. It seems desirable to evaluate such tests for use with lightweight aggregate concretes themselves.

REFERENCE

(64) LYDON, F.D. Concrete mix design. Applied Science Publishers Ltd., London, 1972. pp 148.

Errata

1. Table 2. The average crack spacing at M for gravel and sand
    concrete should be 54.4.

2. Figure 2. The reference should be (14) not (4).

3. Figure 3. The reference should be (23) not (6).

4. Figure 4. The references should be (26, 27) not (1,2);
    Ref.(2) should be Ref. (26).

5. Figure 5. For the 30% R.H. the tensile strain capacity
    scale should be 0, 40, 80, 120, 160.

6. Figure 3. The strains should all be halved, i.e. they should read
    '0, 10, 20, 30, 40, 50, 60'.

Figure 8   Relation between tensile strain capacity and tensile strength (15, 42).

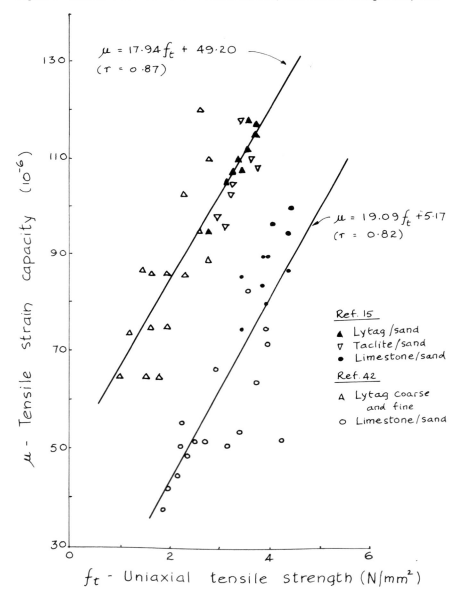

Figure 9 Shrinkage/expansion with drying (52).

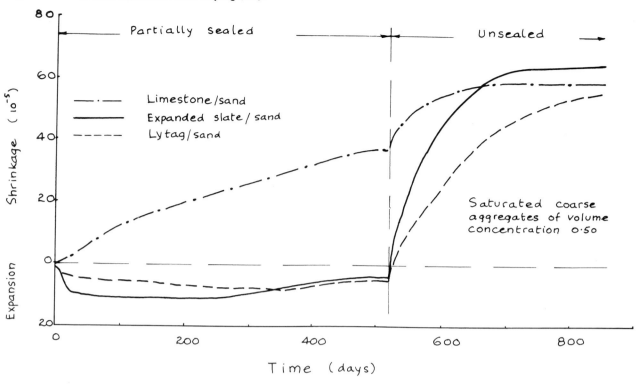

Figure 10   Initial surface absorption (BS 1881) test results.

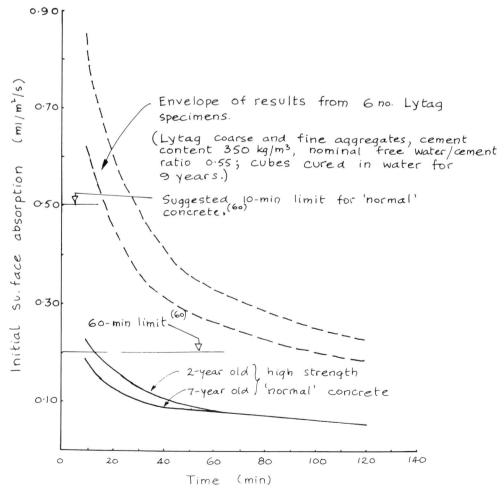

Some structures built in France in lightweight concrete

M Virlogeux
Service d'Études Techniques des Routes et Autoroutes, France

Utilization of lightweight concrete is fairly new in France, but it has been developped for five or six years, leading to the construction of some important structures, mainly bridges.

Concrete International 1980 is an occasion to present the most interesting of them, the bridges of Bruyères sur l'Oise, Calais, Tricastin and Ottmarsheim, the pedestrian bridges of Meylan and Illhof, the Australian Embassy in Paris, and the second Roissy airport.

THE BRIDGE OF BRUYERES SUR L'OISE.

The bridge of Bruyères sur l'Oise, near Paris, was built in 1975, on a diversion of the river Oise. It was built on traditional scaffoldings, before digging the diversion.

It is made of a main span, 71 meters long, with a lightweight concrete central part. The two ends of this main span are embedded in two trapezoidal casings made of normal concrete, which work as side spans.

On one side, the casing in embedded in its foundations. And, on the other side, interposition of neopren supports, between the foundations and the casing, allows for dilatations.

This bridge has been designed by Structec, and built by the contractor Drouard Frères, under the direction of the Service de l'Equipement de la Région Parisienne.

THE BRIDGE OF CALAIS.

Calais' bridge was built in 1976, with the aim of obtaining information on lightweight concrete. Two main aspects have been studied : design and calculation aspects on one side, and construction on the other, that is mainly mixing and concreting.

The bridge has a unique span, 42.575 meters long, made of five prefabricated prestressed beams, interconnected by a general reinforced concrete slab, cast in situ. The whole bridge was built in lightweight concrete.

This bridge has been designed by the S.E.T.R.A. and built by the contractor Quille, under the direction of the Direction Départementale de l'Equipement du Pas-de-Calais.

TRICASTIN'S BRIDGE.

Tricastin's bridge was built over Donzère Mondragon's canal, near Avignon, from the end of 1977 to March 1979. With its 142,50 meters long main span, partly built in lightweight concrete, it is one of the greatest bridges built in France in prestressed concrete. But it is above all remarkable by the very short length of its side spans, which are only 25.25 meters long.

The uplifting reactions on abutments are very important, and may reach 1,200 metric tons. In order to resist these reactions, the bridge has massive ends, which are inserted in the abutments, in the form of huge boxes. The weight of these counterweight abutments is about 1,800 metric tons.

The side spans were built on scaffoldings, after the erection of the lower part of the counterweight abutments. Then the main span was built by the cantilever method, on movable falseworks.

The bridge is a box girder, with two vertical webs.

This bridge has been designed by the contractor, Campenon Bernard Cetra, under the control of the S.E.T.R.A. It has been built by Campenon Bernard Cetra, under the direction of the Direction Départementale de l'Equipement du Vaucluse.

OTTMARSHEIM'S BRIDGE.

Ottmarsheim's bridge has been built over the Alsace's canal, near Mulhouse, between 1977 and 1980. In fact it is made of two separate box girders, each with two vertical webs. Each of these two bridges has five spans, 53 - 171.87 - 23.23 - 143.97 and 37.50 meters long. The central part of the two main spans are built in lightweight concrete.

The two 172 meters long spans are among the greatest in the world in light-weight concrete, along with a bridge over the Rhine in Köhln, in Germany (184 meters), and with Parrott's Ferry bridge, near Sonora, in California (195 meters).

But it is mainly the greatest span in the world built by the cantilever method with prefabricated segments.

The short length of the side spans has led, here also, to uplifting reactions on the abutments. The prefabricated end of the box girder is held by a prefabricated element, called ⊓ owing to its shape, bound to the counterweight abutment by tendons. Each abutment has a weight of about 1,000 metric tons.

This bridge has been designed by the S.E.T.R.A., in collaboration with an architect, A. Arsac. It has been built by the contractor Coignet, who brought some important ameliorations to the project, under the direction of the Direction Départementale de l'Equipement du Haut-Rhin.

MEYLAN'S PEDESTRIAN BRIDGE.

Meylan's pedestrian bridge is now under construction, near Grenoble, since the end of 1979. This is a cable stayed bridge, with three spans, 20 - 79 and 20 meters long. It is a triangular box girder, stayed by an axial stay of cables. The central part of the main span is built in lightweight concrete. The side spans end by concrete boxes, ballasted, which work as counterweight.

Each half bridge is built on scaffoldings, parallel to the river, Isère.
Then the tendons and the cables are tensionned, and the box girder is removed.

Each half bridge is then placed to its final position by rotation around
the foundations under pylon. The end of the side span moves on a roller-path,
to its final position.

The connection between the two half bridges is made by a final in situ
concreting, and by tensionning some tendons.

This bridge has been designed by the contractor Campenon Bernard Cetra,
in collaboration with an architect, A. Arsac, under the control of the
S.E.T.R.A. It has been built for the town of Meylan, under the direction
of the Direction Départementale de l'Equipement de l'Isère.

ILLHOF'S PEDESTRIAN BRIDGE.
_____

At last, Illhof's pedestrian bridge is now under construction, since the
beginning of 1980, in Strasbourg.

This is also a cable stayed pedestrian bridge, with two spans, 20 and 63.50
meters long. It has a single pylon, and two lateral stays of cables. The
deck is made of two lateral ribs connected by a reinforce concrete slab,
and multiple transverse floor beams.

The central part of the main span is built in lightweight concrete.

The main part of the bridge is built on classical scaffoldings, parallel
to the river, Ill. After tensionning the cables and tendons, the bridge is
placed to its final position by rotation around the foundations of the pylon.
The end of the deck moves on a roller-path, to its final position.

The great cantilever is then connected to a short part ot the deck, on abutment, built on scaffolding in its final position, by a final concreting, and
by tensionning some tendons.

The end of the short span has the shape of a box and is ballasted, to work
as a counterweight.

This bridge has been designed by the contractor Campenon Bernard Cetra,
with the help of an architect, A. Arsac, under the control of the S.E.T.R.A.
It has been built for the town of Strasbourg, under the direction of the
technical services of the Communauté Urbaine de Strasbourg.

AUSTRALIAN EMBASSY IN PARIS.
_____

The floors of the Australian Embassy, in Paris, were built with prefabricated
prestressed beams, built in lightweight concrete.

These beams have been concreted in plastic castings, made from a wood matrix.
Their shape have been determined by the architect, Hany Seidler.

Finally, 175 beams have been prefabricated, for 7000 square meters floor.

Each beam was prestressed by a single 12 T 13 tendon.

The beams were prefabricated by the contractor Bouygues, and placed by the
general contractor, Oger.

SECOND ROISSY'S AIRPORT.

The greatest French construction, in lightweight concrete, is the second Roissy's airport, near Paris.

This second airport is composed of six units on a single line, served by a succession of access viaducts. Each of these units is constituted by 18 blocks, 9 on each side of the access viaducts system.

Only the first unit of 18 blocks, and the first 9 blocks of the second unit are now under construction.

Each block is covered by a box girder shell, with two main webs, under which are the supports, and two lateral webs.

These shells are built in lightweight concrete. They are cast at the floor level, except for the upper member. When they are tensionned, they are placed to their final level by a system of four elevators.

The upper member of the shells is cast in situ, in the final position.

This structure has been designed by the Paris Airport's architect, P. Andreu. The contractor Bouygues is in charge of the construction, under the direction of Paris Airport, the Société Française de Précontrainte being consulting engineer.

Figure 1   The bridge of Bruyères sur l'Oise. Longitudinal section.

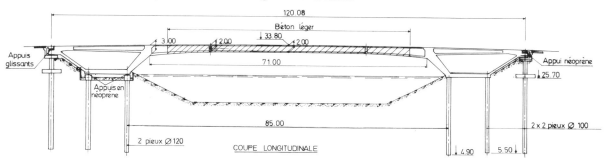

Photo 1   The bridge of Bruyères sur l'Oise.

Figure 2   The bridge of Bruyères sur l'Oise. Cross-section.

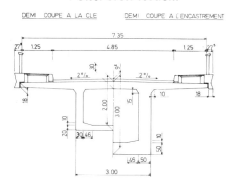

Figure 3   Calais' bridge. Longitudinal section.

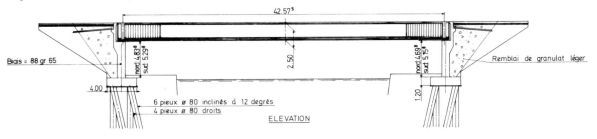

Figure 4   Calais' bridge. Cross-section.

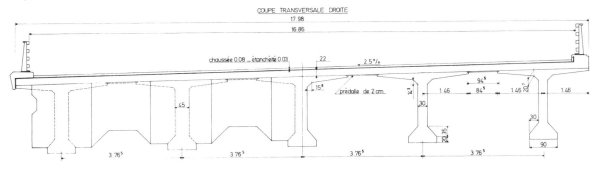

Photo 2   Calais' bridge.

Figure 5   Trincastin's bridge. Longitudinal section.

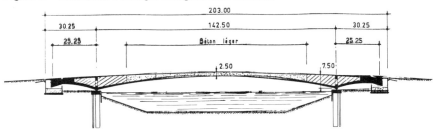

Figure 6   Trincastin's bridge. Cross-section.

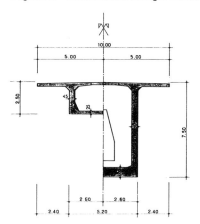

Figure 7   Trincastin's bridge. Abutments.

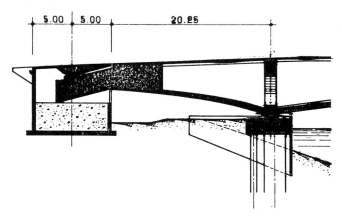

Photo 3   Trincastin's bridge.

Figure 8   Ottmarsheim's bridge. Longitudinal section.

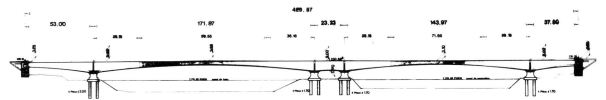

Figure 9   Ottmarsheim's bridge. Cross-section.

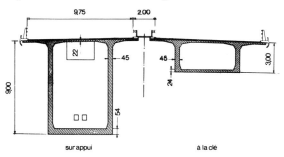

sur appui   à la clé

coupe transversale

Figure 10 Ottmarsheim's bridge. Abutments.

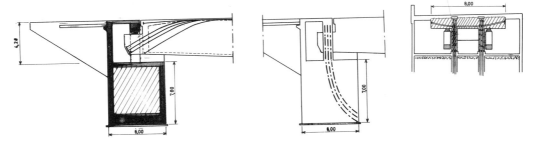

Photo 4 Ottmarsheim's bridge.

Figure 11 Meylan's pedestrian bridge. Longitudinal section.

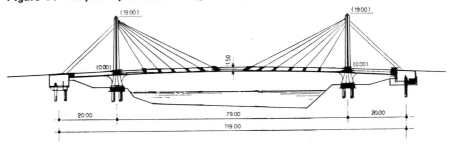

Figure 12 Meylan's pedestrian bridge. Cross-section.

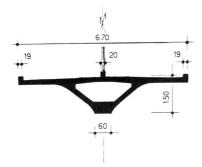

Photo 5 Meylan's pedestrian bridge.

Figure 13 Illhof's pedestrian bridge. Longitudinal section.

Figure 14 Illhof's pedestrian bridge. Cross-section.

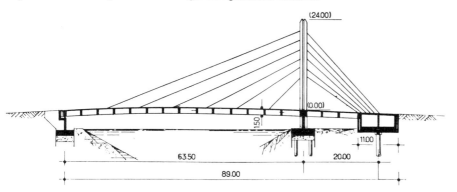

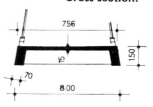

Photo 6 Model of Illhof's pedestrian bridge.

Photo 7 Prefabricated beams on stock.

Photo 8 Australian Embassy.

Figure 15 Second Roissy's Airport. Plan.

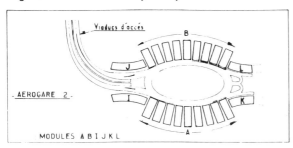

Figure 16 Second Roissy's Airport. Elevation principle.

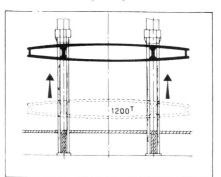

Figure 17   Second Roissy's Airport. Cross-section of a shell.

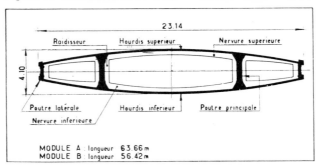

23.14

Raidisseur   Hourdis superieur   Nervure superieure

4.10

Poutre laterale   Hourdis inferieur   Poutre principale
Nervure inferieure

MODULE A : longueur 63.66 m
MODULE B : longueur 56.42 m

Photo 10   One of the four elevators, in position.

Photo 9   General view of the construction.

General discussion

Professor H WEIGLER (Institut fur Massivbau, Technische Hochschule Darmstadt,
Germany FR):   I should like to make a contribution to the item Lightweight
Aggregate Concrete, Foamed Concrete.   As mentioned by Mr Weber, the density
of structural lightweight aggregate concrete can be reduced considerably by
air entrainment in the matrix.   With preformed foams, made with protein-
foaming agents, we could attain in concretes of fluid consistencies air void
contents of up to 25 per cent by volume, with the ratio of dry density to
compressive strength being more favourable, the lower the aggregate particle
density.   As an example, to produce a dry density of 800 kg/m^3, with
aggregates of 0.6 particle density, would require approximately 20 per cent air
voids, and the material would attain a compressive strength of about 8 MPa.
With aggregates of 1.1 particle density, approximately 45 per cent by volume of
foam would be needed and the concrete would attain a strength of only about 2.0 MPa.
For such mixes, it is possible to attain ratios of concrete dry density to
strength within the range 1200:30 to 700:5.   In addition to strength
properties, the deformational characteristics, the bond between reinforcement
and concrete and carbonation effects were investigated.   Shrinkage was found to
be increased by a factor of between 1.3 and 2.0 in relation to normal weight
concrete, while specific creep increased greatly with decreasing compressive
strength and increasing air voids content.   The bond strength between ribbed
reinforcing bars and concrete decreases with increasing air voids content in
approximately the same proportion as does the compressive strength.
However, it is at least equal to that of normal weight concrete of the same
strength.

With regard to the protection of the reinforcement against corrosion, the water:cement ratio of normal concrete is limited to 0.75 in the German standards.   The rate of carbonation which can be expected to occur is not exceeded in lightweight aggregate foamed concrete provided the dry density is not less than 850 kg/m^3.   In all, we have found that such concretes can be used for the construction of heat insulating walls with a load-bearing or stiffening function.   More details can be found in the Paper published in Betonwerk + Fertigteil - Technik Nos. 3 and 4/1980.

C FORDER (Tarmac Eastern Region, UK):

Professor Emery, in his paper on the use of pelletised expanded slag aggregates for concrete masonry production referred, obviously, to the practice as carried on in North America, where comparatively high-density concretes are being used and curing is almost invariably carried out by auto-claving.

In the United Kingdom, we tend to use considerably lower densities for our block manufacture and the need for this makes the early age strength requirement much more critical.   This, in turn, requires a very careful selection and blending of aggregates to produce the optimum particle size distribution.

A certain amount of work is being done by my own company, Tarmac, in the marketing process for pelletised slag.   We have carried out several trials with the leading block manufacturers in the United Kingdom and have been able to establish a series of mix design parameters which not only suit the material but can be modified and adjusted to suit the characteristics of individual types of block machine and different block specifications.

Professor Emery also mentioned the high workability of pelletised slag concrete which he associated with particle surface shape and texture.   For these semi-compacted block concretes this property is reflected in the ease and speed at which even very highly complicated moulds can be filled and the small compactive effort needed to ensure regular distribution and accurate extrusion without excessive density.   This is very important in the UK where the Building Regulations impose strict limits on thermal transmittance through external walls. In low rise housing, particularly, it is also the practice to use comparatively slender masonry units, of the order of 100 mm in total thickness, and to use these as the principal thermal insulating medium.   Thus thermal conductivity is of prime importance in lightweight block manufacture and all forms of lightweight concrete cladding.

Lightweight slag aggregates generally, whether they be pelletised or foamed, are officially accepted in the United Kingdom as having a unique density and thermal conductivity relationship.   In the case of the current vesicular foam slag this conductivity is now recognised as being about 0.75 times that of the average for all other masonry materials of equal density and moisture content.

Tarmac commissioned a range of tests with laboratories throughout the country to investigate whether this phenomenon also occurred with pelletised concrete and to compare it directly with the known and accepted performance of the ordinary vesicular foam slag.   Although the results were somewhat variable, we have been able to construct a thermal conductivity/density relationship from a very large number of results obtained by various methods of test. This relationship shows that the conductivity of pelletised slag concretes is - as Professor Emery mentioned very briefly - as low as slightly less than two-thirds of the average for all other materials, which is a most useful attribute in these times of energy conservation.

Further research is also being carried out by the Building Research Establishment to investigate the structural properties of the material, with particular reference to UK practice.

DR P SULLIVAN (Imperial College, UK):
The object of my brief contribution is to bring to the notice of the Congress what appears to be a point of controversy about the bond and shear characteristics of reinforced lightweight aggregate concrete.   I have two

illustrations of failure cracks on reinforced normal weight and lightweight concrete beams tested in flexure to failure and I shall discuss their respective behaviour both at 20°C and at elevated temperatures.

The tests were carried out on a 25 mm x 75 mm cross section, 850 mm long beams containing two 6 mm diameter plain mild steel bars without shear stirrups. Other beams containing shear stirrups were also tested but the interesting results which allow examination of the failure behaviour of the concrete within the shear zones are given by the beams without shear stirrups. The 28-day cube strength of both normal weight - (density 2340 kgs/m^3) - and lightweight concrete - (density 1650 kgs/m^3) - was in the region of 40 N/m^2, and the ultimate load-bearing capacities of both types of reinforced concrete beams containing stirrups were similar.

Further details on the above and comparisons of other properties may be found listed under references (1), (2), (3) and (4).

(1)　'The Effects of transient and steady state Temperature on Concrete' PhD London 1973 - Akhtauzzaman AA.

(2)　'The Short-term Structural Behaviour of a Lightweight Aggregate Concrete at Elevated Temperature' PhD London 1977 - Labani JM.

(3)　'Flexural Behaviour of Plain and Reinforced Lightweight Concrete Beams up to 600°C' Sullivan, PJE and Labani JM - Cement & Concrete Research 1974. 2. 231-237.

(4)　'Developments in Concrete Technology' - editor F D Lydon, Chapter I 'The Effects of Temperature on Concrete' by PJE Sullivan.

A number of reinforced concrete beams made with gravel aggregate were tested to failure at different temperatures. At 20°C diagonal tension cracks developed outside the loading points, together with a few flexural cracks within the pure bending zone. The ultimate strengths of these beams were slightly less than the beams containing stirrups where bending failure had occurred. Shear failure also occurred at highet temperatures and a steep reduction in strength occurred at 350°C. Although the beam-carrying capacity beyond 550°C reduced considerably, flexural failure resulted due to the increased plasticity of both the steel and the concrete.

For lightweight aggregate concrete containing sintered pulverized fuel ash -
quite a different behaviour resulted.   At 20°C, failure occurred suddenly
at 79.5 per cent of the flexural failure strength.   Bond slip occurred prior
to a horizontal crack appearing at the level of the reinforcement.   Some
authorities ascribe the splitting that occurs at the level of reinforcement
as a tensile weakness of lightweight concrete;   others describe this as the
initiation of shear compression failure which resulted immediately after.
In these tests it was possible to clamp the reinforcing bars and distribute
their load against the ends of the concrete beam - but this did not prevent
bond or tensile splitting failure.   The ultimate strength of these beams
remained sensibly constant up to 300°C, and there was a drop thereafter.
The beams that did not contain shear stirrups showed a steep decrease in
strength at just below 100°C.   This did not occur in the reinforced concrete
beams with stirrups.

The flexural strength of unreinforced concrete beams was also investigated.
A steep decrease in flexural strength occurred between 60°C and 90°C.   At
higher temperatures, the flexural strength recovered, until, at around 400°C,
the strength exceeded the 20°C value by 10 per cent.   Even at 600°C, the
maximum strength loss was only 12 per cent.

Pull out tests were then performed on 6 mm plain mild steel bars embedded
in 50 mm of lightweight aggregate concrete prisms 100 mm square.   The results
of these indicated that the average peak bond strength at 20°C was 2.36 N/mm^2.
This is in excess of the anchorage bond strength, and also the flexural bond
strength allowed in CP 110 for normal weight concrete.   Beyond the peak bond
strength, the pullout strength gradually decreased to a constant value varying
between 40 per cent and 60 per cent of the peak value.

Bearing in mind the inferior bond behaviour of the lightweight aggregate
reinforced beams tested in flexure and described earlier, it would be unrealistic
to adopt the peak pullout strength as the bond strength.   It may be that the lower
value would give a better assessment of the bond strength.

The pullout strength at higher temperature showed a reduction at about 100°C, or just below 100°C, but this again recovers at higher temperatures. At around 200°C, the so-called peak bond strength is 40 per cent higher than the 20 per cent value between 200°C and 300°C.

The picture that emerges from these tests indicates that by comparison to normal weight concrete, lightweight concrete has:

1. A lower flexural bond strength at normal temperatures;
2. A very low flexural concrete strength between 60°C and 100°C.

However, with approximately designed tensile reinforcement and stirrups, this apparent discontinuity at these comparative low temperatures is eliminated and the performance of the beams improved.

To conclude, therefore, it is still possible for reinforced lightweight aggregate concrete to perform as well as normal-weight concrete, if not better, by adopting appropriate design, and at the same time taking advantage of the superior behaviour of lightweight concrete at temperatures above 100°C. If the design engineer treats the material as normal weight concrete, introducing solely arithmetical factors, the full benefits of lightweight aggregate cannot be exploited, but on the contrary, runs the risk of producing structural elements with built-in weaknesses, and ultimately inferior products.

K VINE-LOTT (Thermal Structures Limited, UK):

I should like to say something about current developments on mix design for structural foam concretes in the 1200 - 1500 kg/m^3 density range made, using foaming agents and foam generators.

The benefit of this material is improved thermal properties, ease of placing, lightweight, and considerably increased workability.

The material can be pumped directly into moulds and differs from 'gas' concretes in two important respects. It has a closed cell structure which results in reduced water permeability and when used in bulk it produces a relatively slow shrinkage, moisture and thermal movements. Thus the only movements are those in the long term which result in stresses being induced and retained in the material.   Manufacturing is simplified since the concrete can be air dried.

I have a selection of slides which show the sorts of ways in which it is being used.

Precast Work: In Italy they are manufacturing panels of up to 30 sq m in area in a single casting.   The panels, forming complete house sides, weigh 5 or 6 tonnes and can be lifted and handled complete.   The illustration shows a German operation, but the technique is the same.

Block Making: It is not an easy process to manufacture blocks from this material since it is very fluid and sets relatively slowly.   Thus the traditional egg-laying type machine is not applicable and the split block process is used.

Houses being built in situ and precast using two layers of lightweight concrete separated by polyurethane foam manufactured as a single unit: The polyurethane foam is placed in the shutters, and as long as the very free flowing concrete is balanced with reasonable care, then both sides can be filled at the same time. K-values of approximately 0.28 are achieved with this form of construction. The material is now well established and over 1 million cubic metres have been made and placed throughout the world over the past four years.   The properties are well tested and we are well past the experimental stage. The material itself is very easily placed.

However, a few problems exist, the main ones being the following:-

(i)   Density/strength relationship.   Good quality control is essential to prevent the density reducing to a value which would result in unacceptable loss of strength.   Thus, a proper foaming agent must be used, together with a modern mixer which provides sufficient control. It is not just a matter of pouring some foam into the first machine that comes to hand; if this does happen, then the concrete should not be used structurally.   We have developed microprocessor controlled machines to get over this problem.

(ii) Bond strength.   Here, I agree with Dr Sullivan's remarks.
The flexural and tensile strengths of foamed concretes are lower,
resulting in reduced bond.   To combat this we always use mesh - as
illustrated on the earlier photograph.

(iii) Lower modulus of elasticity.   Since this is also lower, design must
be carefully considered.

(iv) Sand gradings.   It should be noted that there should be very little
at the bottom end, less than 0.25, and the denser the concrete, the
coarser the grading.   Over 8 mm it cannot be pumped.   It is not that
it cannot be used.   It is just that it cannot be pumped.   Foam
concrete is being used in the UK, but so far very little.   Most of the
work seems to have been done overseas.

C HOBBS (John Laing Research and Development Limited, UK):

I shall not speak on any one topic, but on all of them in general.
I am really addressing the UK audience particularly, and specifically those
people in the UK audience who are not researchers.

We began developing the Lytag process 27 years ago in 1953, and we spent
seven years, from 1953 to 1960, testing and demonstrating that with that
aggregate good quality concrete could be made, and that good quality structures
could be built with that concrete.   In 1960, we built our first factory.
Here we are in 1980, twenty years after, and twenty-seven years after we began,
and where have we got to with Lytag, pelletised foam slag Leca, and the other
manufacture lightweight aggregates in the UK?   Very largely they are merely
substitutes for clinker, an aggregate used to manufacture what was originally
called a breeze block.

Admittedly these aggregates have been used in a number of major structures,
and with completely satisfactory results.   But as Mr Horler said in Session 1,
they represent no more than about 2 per cent of the total structural market,
so not much impression has been made in that 27-year period.   Someone mentioned
that lightweight aggregate concretes were being used very much earlier than
that, and we had some very good examples of their use in 1920.

68

There is something wrong, somewhere, in our rate of application of innovation of this kind and the way in which these materials are exploited. Here I find myself very much in sympathy with Mr Holm, who said that we should do a lot less testing and a lot more building, start talking a great deal more about the successes that have been achieved and the realities of the achievements, and what actually has happened instead of worrying ourselves too much about details of bond strength, long-term creep, or such topics. We have had a lot of the data now available for a very long time indeed, and we seem to be unable to translate it to our designers in such a way that they can make use of it. We have to recognise that lightweight concrete is still a second thought to our designers in that they think first in terms of traditional reinforced concrete for a given use. If they happen to have a special problem they will then consider lightweight as a particular method of solution. Lightweight concretes have not yet reached the stage where people recognise them as legitimate additions to their armoury to be considered on every design occasion as a possible method of solving the problem. I know our industry is craft-based, and I know that it is conservative in its approach, but if we go on at this speed of innovation, we shall be going backwards very shortly. The scope for major developments in concrete is greater now than it has ever been and this Congress highlights very much that that is the case. We have newer, improved admixtures which allow us to do remarkable things to concrete in its fresh stage. We have a whole range of new aggregates which enhance properties in the hardened stage. We are beginning, also, to be offered new forms of reinforcement. It would be beneficial if these materials could be brought together and exploited in a constructive manner to lead the industry into the twentieth century. But when will it happen? Who will do it? How long will we have to wait? Will it be the twenty-second century?

R C VALORE (Valore Research Associates, USA):

I would like to make some comments with respect to pelletised slag as described by Professor Emery and discussed by Mr Forder.

Pelletised slag is used in Hamilton, Ontario as an aggregate mainly for autoclaved lightweight blocks. I am well aware of the fine things that have been done with pelletised slag in France, where a density of the order of, say, 1300 kgs/m^3 can be obtained. Unfortunately, in Hamilton, Ontario, it is not possible to make a concrete block that has an average density less than 1700 kgs/m^3 on a day basis. This is just high enough to fail to meet the requirements for a lightweight block as required by ASTM.

We have argued with manufacturers who claim they can achieve lower densities but we have never attained them. The particular plant making blocks from this aggregate happens to be located strategically two miles from a source of supply. This is one of the plants to which Professor Emery referred, that is now in receivership, but I do not believe that we can blame the receivership on the density of the slag since they went into receivership in the year in which they exceeded by a considerable margin the total volume of units produced in their entire history.

With respect to Mr Forder, he referred to autoclaving being the predominant type of curing in North America. In fact, autoclaving reached a peak of some 20 per cent of production, whereas it is now down to 15 per cent, and is reducing rapidly. No new autoclaving plants are being built for lightweight aggregate or normal weight aggregate blocks, and the same companies that I helped some twenty years ago to start autoclaving are calling upon my services as a consultant to finish with the process. We would appreciate the aerated concrete industry evolving a process that would allow these excellent autoclaves to be used to make aerated concrete, particularly if the process could use even a small portion of our 50 million tonnes of fly ash generated annually.

With respect to lightweight blocks, they would be considered as heavy blocks in North America. The Hamilton, Ontario block is not typical. In the West, blocks are made out of pumice to achieve densities down to approximately 850 kgs/m^3. There are at least two producers of expanded shale who make

their product light enough to produce a block of 1000 kgs/m^3 density.   Our
specifications require a loadbearing block to have a compressive strength of
the order of 2000 or 2200 p.s.i., (approximately 14 N/mm^2), based on net area.

There are many areas in the US where the lightweight block is the only type
of block produced, for example, in the South, on the West Coast, and in
certain parts of the Mid-West.   Energy conservation has made such an impact
that our requirements in certain States today for U-factor or thermal
transmittance are some 30 per cent below those of the United Kingdom
which only requires a U-factor of 1.0 watts/m^2 in the walls of domestic
housing.   The State of Connecticut, for example, requires some 30 per cent
below this, and although there has been some initial over-reaction to the
energy situation now, we are taking it seriously.   As Mr Holm said in an
earlier publication, we must consider not only the energy expended in producing
certain lightweight aggregates, but also the energy saved in the use of such
products which should be thought of as an investment that pays for itself
many times over.

G J OSBORNE (Building Research Station, UK):   In reply to a comment made
by Mr Forder.
The Inorganic Materials Division at BRE, Garston, has a current research programme
designed to evaluate the properties of pelletized slag as a lightweight aggregate
in concrete, and as a cementitious material in slag cement.   As Mr Forder
mentioned, BRE has a co-operative research agreement with Tarmac Roadstone
(Northern) Ltd, who are one of the producers of pelletized slag in the UK, for
investigating the use of pelletized slag as a coarse and as a fine aggregate in
structural lightweight concrete.   This comparative work is proceeding well,
and a range of concrete mixes has been made and tested at BRE to assess strength
development and durability.   The durability studies, as yet at an early stage,
include long-term tests carried out on BRE's marine and soft-water exposure sites.
The use of pelletized slag in slag cements is also being investigated using BS
mortar cube tests and small-scale test methods to assess strength development

and sulphate resistance.   Preliminary results are encouraging for both
prospective uses of pelletized slag, but more detailed work needs to be carried
out on some new sources of slag such as that from Redcar.

P POITEVIN (Spie-Batignolles, France):

Professor Emery has raised a question on slag cement in Session II.
He said that at his University they had tested 50/50 mixtures of clinker
and slag.   Such mixtures have been tested in Paris - perhaps as long
ago as 1950 - and the conclusions were that such mixtures were interesting
but that for concrete in sulphated soils the best solution was the
incorporation of the highest proportion of slag.   It is the French formula
of the C L K with at least 80 per cent of slag and less than 20 per cent of
clinker.   This formula was tested in Paris, for use on the Metro some fifty
years ago, and it gives excellent durability in sulphated soils.

It is an international problem.   In many countries we meet sulphated oils,
and slag cements - with a very high percentage of slag - are an economical soluti

PROFESSOR J J EMERY (McMaster University, Canada):

In my presentation I pointed out that it should never be assumed that slags
from one country, or even within countries, are the same.   There is a simple
reason why we can use a 50/50 blend, based on five years testing, in that we
have a low alumina slag and have tested it with our highest C_3A cement. When
the French have said that one must use 80 per cent, the Germans 70 per cent,
etc., this is to cover all of their cements and all of their slags.
Therefore, there is no contradiction with our findings.

I must acknowledge, of course, that in North America we are far behind the
Europeans in the use of separately ground or interground slag cements.

Regarding the densities of blocks in Hamilton and the use of autoclaves;
in Canada we are still using autoclaved products because we have a very severe
winter climate.   The question of densities is one of fact in that 80 to 90
per cent of the blocks manufactured are heavyweight blocks, and the pellets are

used in these to give a more efficient block in terms of cost. The lightweight block market in Canada is not very large.   I may have given the impression that it is the bulk market, but the bulk market is in heavyweight blocks because of our structural requirements.   All blocks manufactured in Canada are manufactured to structural requirements, although about 90 per cent are used in non-structural applications.

W TENOUTASSE (University of Brussels, Belgium)

Chairman, Gentlemen.   I shall surprise you because I am disappointed in that I have not had an answer to a lot of the questions I had before coming here.   I shall speak about my country, Belgium, but I am sure that the same problems are to be found in Germany, France and The Netherlands, etc.

A few years ago, in Belgium, a very large company intended to start building a new plant to make lightweight aggregates based on the use of fly ash. However, a very clever economist concluded that we could not produce a single tonne of fly ash in Belgium for a number of years.   Now, even in our little country, we have a million tonnes of fly ash and do not know what to do with it! Later the same company decided to use shale from coal mines since in Belgium we have a large number of coal mines.   Now they have nearly all been closed and we import coal from Poland and the US but that is another problem, so they commenced production of structural lightweight aggregate with shale from coal mines, but the new plant has now been closed for reasons of economics.

In my country we have a lot of slag, since our steel industry is still very important.   However, we no longer make foamed slag, even though the material is manufactured without expending additional energy.   I do not understand the reasons for this but can conclude only that, although we publish reports of many investigations into the use of lightweight aggregate, such reports do not appear to significantly influence the use and production of the material.

W G CORLEY (Portland Cement Association, USA)

In listening to today's programme, I was quite interested in all of the testing that was reported, and the fact that some of the results depended on how the tests were performed.   Such results are quite useful in evaluating the properties of the lightweight aggregate and in determining its acceptability, but are not very relevant to the performance.   For example, it was pointed out that questions have been raised about the strain capacity of concrete. That is important in columns, where the strength of the steel must be developed before the column reaches its strength, but the strains that were reported were for plain concrete without confining reinforcement.   No column is built without ties, at least, and if they are taken into account we find lightweight aggregate has more than adequate strain capacity.

It was also noted that there were questions about the shear strength of lightweight concrete.   In the US, there is only one system in which stirrups can be omitted, and this special system has a good record of performance. In all other structures stirrups must be used, and where there are stirrups, then the strength of the member is quite predictable and adequate.

Lightweight concrete is being used as a structural material just like any other, using requirements which are stated in the United States Building Codes. It has a predictable performance and can be manufactured in strengths up to 100 N/mm^2.   It is not a mysterious material, but we consider it as just another structural concrete.   Its only restriction is the one just referred to, namely economics.   When it is economically reasonable to use lightweight aggregate concrete, then it is used.

DR P SULLIVAN (Imperial College, London):

I should like to address my contribution to Mr Gerritse with regard to his statement that lightweight concrete is susceptible to spalling.   This phenomenon is also known to occur with limestone and gravel concrete. Explosive spalling has occurred at relatively low temperatures on panels with both types of concrete during fire tests in the UK.   Accidental explosive spalling also occurred about ten years ago in a furnace in my laboratory on a gravel concrete beam, dimension 50 mm x 75 mm x 850 mm long, which had been previously left in water for a considerable time. This instigated research into parameters affecting explosive spalling on gravel concretes which included type of curing, curing time, heating rate, specimen size, and manner of heating. The rate of heating was nowhere as steep as the standard fire rate of heating. A temperature of about 400° at a fast rate of heating was reached in about 40 minutes, and by and large explosive spalling occurred between 30 and 40 minutes, depending on the rate of heating.

Figure 1 shows the furnace temperature against time in minutes.

Figure 1   Time-furnace temperature plot for different heating rates.

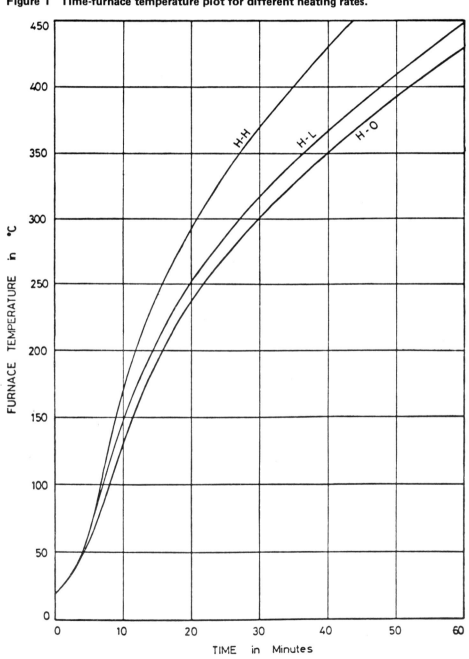

Figure 2   Typical time-temperature curve for a specimen.

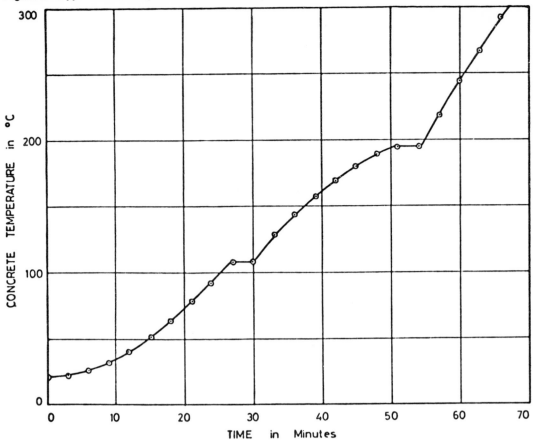

Figure 2   shows average temperature of the concrete beam against time.

<u>Note:</u>   the initial rate of increase in concrete
temperature up to just over 100°C, after
which the temperature remains constant as
the water evaporates.
There is also another constant temperature
part at around 200°C where explosive spalling
normally occurred when the right conditions existed.

Ignoring for the present the significance of the ordinates in Figure 3
I would like you to observe the dividing lines between spalling occurring
(below the lines) and the concrete remaining intact (1).   It will be
noticed that for the water cured specimens explosive spalling occurred for
concrete up to an age of 30 days at a fast rate of heating.   At a low
rate of heating explosive spalling occurred in concrete beams, not older
than 5 days.

(1)   Sullivan PJE and Zaman AAA.   Explosive Spalling of Concrete
exposed to High Temperatures.   Proceedings of the 1st International
Conference on Structural Mechanics in Reactor Technology H1/5 Berlin 1971.

Figure 3 Calculated stress due to steam pressure at various ages.

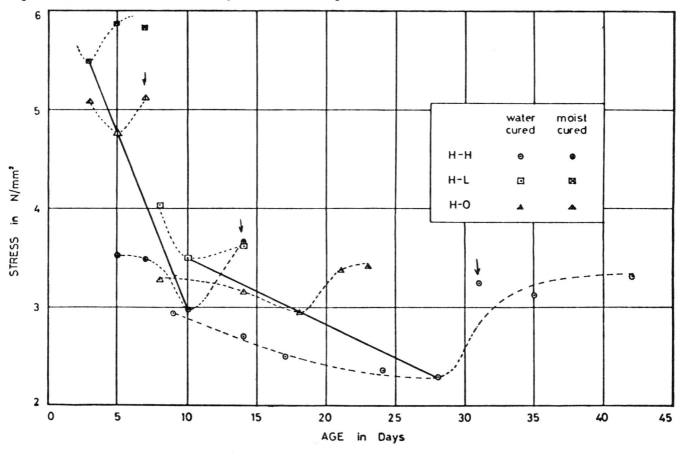

DR P GRUBL (Institut für Bauingenieurwesen II, Germany):

Mr Gerritse showed experimental results from tests with normal weight

concrete and lightweight concrete involving the measurement of compressive

and splitting tensile strengths.   In the diagrams presented, the difference

between the normal weight concrete and lightweight concrete was obvious.

For an engineer designing and constructing with lightweight aggregate concrete

accurate information on the properties of the concrete is necessary.   In

addition, it is helpful to have some knowledge of the fracture behaviour.

We recently made some further investigations into this problem, and from the

results we obtained a better understanding of the material behaviour.   I should

like to present a short summary of those results.

It is very helpful when regarding concrete to simplify it as a two-phase

material with one phase represented by the mortar and the other by the aggregate.

Concrete can then be characterised by the ratio of the modulus of deformation of

mortar and aggregate (Fig 1).   With normal weight concrete the modulus of

Figure 1.

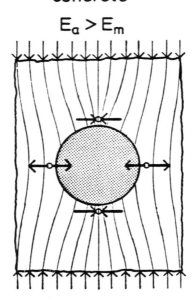

Normalweight concrete

$E_a > E_m$

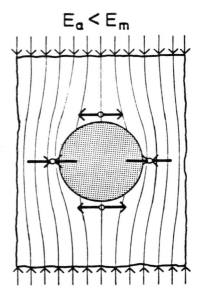

Leightweight aggregate concrete

$E_a < E_m$

⟵—○—⟶ Tension

—⟶×⟵— Compression

deformation of the aggregate is usually greater than that of the mortar whereas with lightweight aggregate concrete the situation is reversed.   The difference in stiffness ratio causes a different transmission of internal forces when the concrete is loaded externally.   With normal weight concrete the internal forces are concentrated through the aggregate, whereas with lightweight aggregate concrete a large part of the internal force is transmitted around the aggregate. Due to this, the regions in which the tensile stresses will be generated under unified states of stress are situated at the side of aggregate particles for normal weight concrete, whereas with lightweight aggregate concrete this region lies above and below the particles.

Once cracks have started in the lightweight aggregate concrete, some five kinds of fracture (types 1 to 5) can be distinguished.   Figure 2 illustrates the compressive strength of the lightweight concrete as a function of the mortar strength.

In the lower strength range, the strengths of concrete and mortar are similar. This is because the modulus of deformation of the aggregate is larger than the one of the mortar which is a condition found particularly at early stages. This situation is then similar to that of normal weight concrete (fracture type 1). Cracks arise and propagate along the surface between mortar and aggregate and

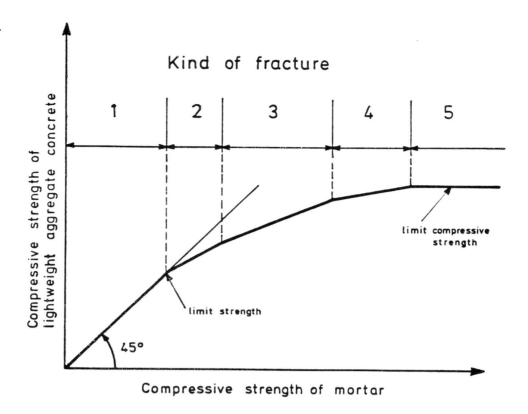

Figure 2.

Kind of fracture

1   2   3   4   5

Compressive strength of lightweight aggregate concrete

limit compressive strength

limit strength

45°

Compressive strength of mortar

when the stiffness of the mortar becomes greater – in Figure 2 it is above the limit strength – cracks are generated above and below due to the change of stress distribution previously described, although a further increase of the external load is possible.   To maintain the internal force balance it can be assumed that the force which is not transmitted further in the cracked region will be distributed to the aggregate (Figure 3).   If the strength of the interface between aggregate and mortar is not sufficient this redistribution is not possible and the cracks will propagate around the aggregate (fracture type 2). In the other case, the distributed force increases and the tensile stress in the aggregate is also increased.   Failure will occur when the tensile strength of the aggregate is attained which leads to the fracture types 3 and 4.   With a mortar of very high tensile strength it is possible that the tensile strength of the aggregate will be reached without cracks in the mortar.   In this case, and other things being equal, the compressive strength of the lightweight aggregate concrete is only generated by the tensile strength of the aggregate (fracture type 5).   With a mortar and lightweight aggregate both of high tensile strengths it is possible for the compressive strength to be higher than with normal weight concrete of a comparable composition.

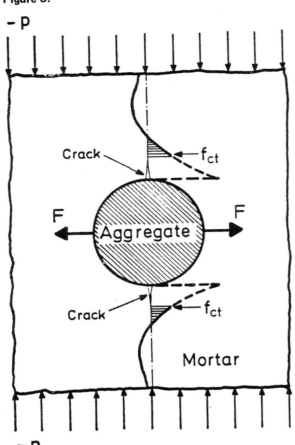

Figure 3.

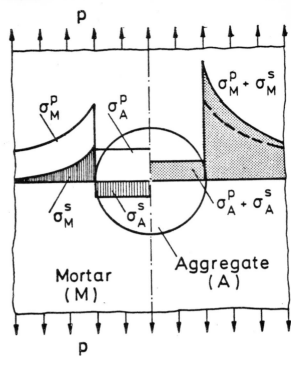

Figure 4.

p..... due to external load

s...... due to shrinkage

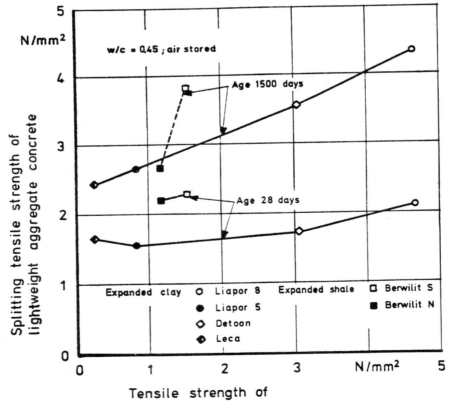

Figure 5.

Tensile strength of
the aggregate, grainsize 8/16 mm

Mr Gerritse also mentioned that with normal weight concrete the influence of drying is less than with lightweight aggregate concrete. This effect can also be explained using the model presented (Figure 4). When the mortar loses water a shrinkage stress will be generated around the aggregate. With lightweight aggregate concrete the shrinkage in the vicinity of the aggregates is greater than with normal weight concrete due mainly to the water absorption of the porous aggregates. This shrinkage stress is superimposed on the tensile stress generated by the external loading. In such a case the tensile strength of the mortar is lowered, similarly, when testing the flexural tensile strength with an air-stored beam. If the moisture content of the lightweight aggregate concrete has reached equilibrium state due to a longer storage period and the shrinkage stress in the vicinity of the aggregates is minimised by relaxation, the lightweight aggregate concrete will reach a tensile strength comparable with that of normal weight concrete. In such a case the tensile strength is also governed by the tensile strength of the aggregate (Figure 5).

A GERRITSE (Hollandsche Beton Groep, The Netherlands):

I was pleased to see that Dr Grubl's paper explained nearly all the modes of performance of lightweight concrete by differences in moduli of deformation. I have heard quite a number of factors in favour of lightweight concrete but its disadvantages must also be recognised. One such concerns the hairline cracks arising on the exposed faces of lightweight concrete structures. I know it is often claimed that they do not exist, but I know that they can be found in Holland and in Munich, for example. This problem could possibly be solved using Dr Grubl's approach.

One comment on explosive spalling in reply to Dr Sullivan. Explosive spalling is mainly due to humidity, and it also relates both to dense concrete and lightweight concrete. But lightweight concrete in its initial stages contains much more water and so is more prone to it. I can assure my audience that it takes at least 6 months to attain a mixture level at which spalling will not occur. How long it will take before the humidity range below which there is no spalling is reached is the subject of a Dutch CUR Report.

Mr Little asked whether it would not be possible to convince the code-making committees to accept grades of lightweight concrete containing natural sands as equal to normal weight concrete.   I have put forward in my paper the Dutch approach which uses ratio coefficients and ratio factors, and by accepting this method the influence of natural sand is accounted for.   Ratio factors solve the problem not only for lightweight concrete but also for fibre reinforced polymer impregnated materials, etc.

B K BARDHAN-ROY (Jan Bobrowski and Partners, UK):

In Mr Forrest's paper an example for calculation of fire resistance has been given.   This shows the advantages of continuity or end fixity. Even the use of nominal anti-crack reinforcement over the support may significantly increase the fire resistance capacity of sections.   The particular example, however, relates to normal weight concrete.   If lightweight aggregate concrete is considered in the same way the result will be even more dramatic.   I have re-calculated the same example and found that instead of two hours' fire resistance as shown the same section with the same reinforcement will have over three hours' fire resistance if lightweight concrete is substituted for dense concrete.

DR A STEINDL (Fa. Wienerberger Baustoffindustrie AG., Austria):

In his paper Mr Bender shows the same unit cost of $150 for heavyweight concrete grade 3ST and lightweight concrete.   Can he explain this?

B BENDER (BVN/STS, USA):

As I understood the question, it was about Table 2, where normal weight concrete has been used in both cases with lightweight concrete only being used for the superstructure with a normal weight concrete substructure.   But heavyweight concrete used more concrete than did the lightweight superstructure. The unit costs are the same because the units in the table - all the concrete used - is heavyweight, but there is less of it when there is a lightweight superstructure.

J C M FORREST (Kenchington Little & Partners, UK):

Might I correct a misapprehension in my paper concerning the Cité
Administrative Building where I referred to the fire protection coating
being applied to both the hollow ribbed floor and to the steel beams.
A delegate from Belgium, Mr A Verkeyn, who has been involved with the
design of this structure, has pointed out that the fire protection applies

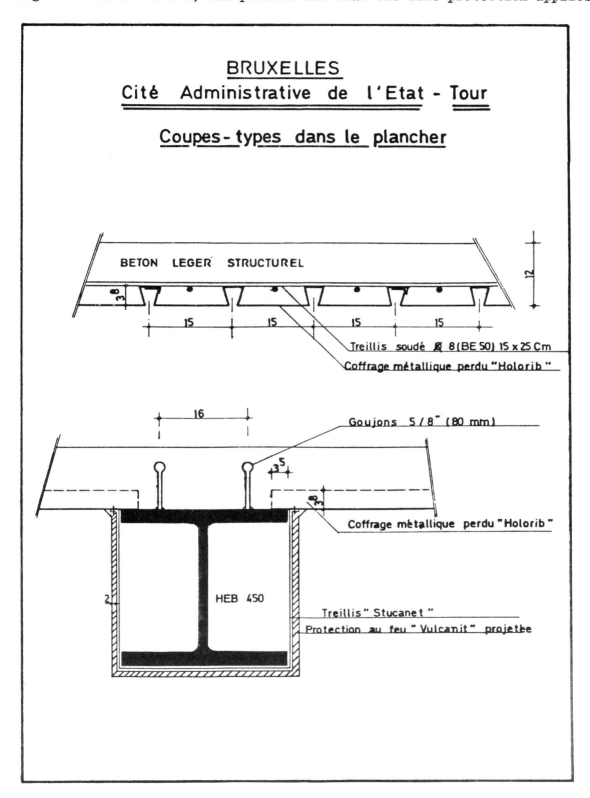

only to the steel beams and not to the hollow ribbed floor.   Consequently,
we are talking only of a mesh around the steel beams, with the Vulcanit
plaster to which I referred being applied to act as fire protection to the
structural steel frame.

(See sketch provided, post Congress, by delegate, A Verkeyn).

K D RAITHBY (Transport and Road Research Laboratory, UK):
Recently a colleague and I have been engaged in reviewing the use of
lightweight concrete in highway bridges.   Our friends from North America
have been rather modest in their statements of the extent of their usage of
lightweight concrete.   When the review was being undertaken, we learned of
over 200 major highway bridges in the US extensively using lightweight concrete.
In Western Europe there were several major bridges, notably from France,
Holland and West Germany.   In Great Britain the total was two road
bridges, only one of these being on the public highway.   I hope that the
future will redress the balance.

J B NEWMAN - Chairman (Imperial College of Science and Technology, London, UK)
This is the end of the Lightweight Concrete Congress of CI'80 and one or two
thoughts are lingering in my mind.

Firstly, one cannot help but be impressed by some of the bridgework in the US,
in Holland and in Germany.   There has certainly been enormous progress
on that front in the last ten years.

Secondly, I should like to support Jan Bobrowski in his plea for a little more
engineering judgement and less mathematics.   This may also deal with some
of the fiery words from Mr Skoyles on the economics of lightweight concrete.
Those in the industry who have considered the use of lightweight concrete
for particular applications have been guided by our engineering judgement.
If this showed us that lightweight concrete provided the best solution then
we used it no matter what our quantity surveyor friends told us.   I would
urge everyone to use the material when they _feel_ that they should be using it.

H Holland, Wimpey Laboratories Limited

Having read Mr Lietch's paper and listened to his presentation, I am
very surprised and somewhat concerned that he only referred to the
corrosion of reinforcement under the sub-heading "unautoclaved aerated
concrete", thus, as I see it, implying that problems with corrosion were
non existent in autoclaved aerated concrete, whereas, both Mr Lietch and
I know that this is not so.

Serious corrosion can and has occurred in external reinforced aerated
concrete wall panels for whatever the reasons, yet the reinforcement was (and
I quote from the then current Trade Literature for the particular unit) "protected
from corrosion by a special coating technique".

Would Mr Lietch like to state whether the 'special coating' is supposed to
provide permanent protection, if not, why not? Would he also like to comment
on the precautions which are still necessary, from delivery of the aerated
units to site, to completion, in order to ensure that such deterioration does
not occur.

Errata (in 'CI80 Lightweight Concrete' – B Bender)

In Table I (page 208) the estimates given in columns 2 and 3 of materials
(line 1), cost of segments on site (line 7) and total superstructure (line 12)
and the totals at the foot of the columns were incorrect. The two columns
should read as follows:

ALTERNATE I Heavyweight Concrete	ALTERNATE II Lightweight Concrete
$ 2,496,024	$ 2,495,180
$ 406,000	$ 451,000
$ 1,453,603	$ 1,032,259
$ 1,453,603	$ 1,032,259
$ 290,720	$ 206,451
$ 203,220	$ 150,000
$ 6,303,170	$ 5,367,149
$ 1,100,157	$ 862,200
$ 653,152	$ 463,326
$ 522,521	$ 370,661
$ 857,637	$ 706,840
$ 9,436,637	$ 7,770,176
$ 2,521,368	$ 2,363,095
$ 529,487	$ 496,250

TOTAL $12,487,492   TOTAL $10,629,521

Table IV (page 211) should read as follows:

Table IV Superstructure materials.

ITEMS	ALTERNATE I HEAVYWEIGHT CONCRETE			ALTERNATE II LIGHTWEIGHT CONCRETE		
	QUANTITY	UNIT COST	TOTAL COST	QUANTITY	UNIT COST	TOTAL COST
1. Superstructure concrete precast	4,825 cuyds	$ 38.00	$183,350	4,825 cuyds	$ 48.00	$231,600
2. Superstructure concrete in situ	165 cuyds	$200.00	$ 33,000	165 cuyds	$210.00	$ 34,650
3. Rebar regular	529,300 lbs	$ .40	$211,700	529,300 lbs	$ .40	$211,700
4. Rebar epoxy-coated	277,000 lbs	$ .70	$158,900	277,000 lbs	$ .70	$158,900
5. P.T. anchors 12 strands	612 pcs	$110.00	$ 67,320	556 pcs	$110.00	$ 61,160
4 strands	1,020 pcs	$ 45.00	$ 45,900	1,020 pcs	$ 45.00	$ 45,900
6. P.T. ducts 3" diameter	50,000 lft	$ .40	$ 20,000	46,000 lft	$ .40	$ 18,400
1¼" diameter	34,000 lft	$ .35	$ 11,900	34,000 lft	$ .35	$ 11,900
7. Strand 270 ksi longitudinal P.T.	600,000 lft	$ .30	$180,000	552,000 lft	$ .30	$165,600
Strand 270 ksi transverse P.T.	100,000 lft	$ .30	$ 30,000	100,000 lft	$ .30	$ 30,000
8. Epoxy (.66/sq.ft. joint area)	16,570 lbs	$ 3.00	$ 49,700	15,000 lbs	$ 3.00	$ 45,000

ALTERNATE I

Cost in 1979	$ 991,780
Cost in 1980	$1,090,958
Cost in 1981	$1,200,053
Cost in 1982	$1,320,059

Cost of material in

$$1981 = \frac{335 * 1,200,053}{558} = \$\ 720,462$$

Cost of material in

$$1982 = \frac{223 * 1,320,059}{558} = \frac{\$\ 527,550}{\$1,248,012}$$

Total cost of 2 bridges = $2,496,024

ALTERNATE II

Cost in 1979	$1,015,000
Cost in 1980	$1,116,500
Cost in 1981	$1,228,150
Cost in 1982	$1,350,965

Cost of material in

$$1981 = \frac{335 * 1,228,150}{398} = \$1,033,744$$

Cost of material in

$$1982 = \frac{63 * 1,350,965}{398} = \frac{\$\ 213,846}{\$1,247,590}$$

Total cost of 2 bridges = $2,495,180

Sprayed concrete

General discussion

MATERIALS AND PERFORMANCE

P POITEVIN (Spie-Batignolles, France):

I have occasion to raise with Mr Humphries the quality control of sprayed concrete in tunnels.   In France we use cylinders instead of cubes, and we prefer to core in a smaller diameter so as to have a ratio of length to diameter that approaches 2.0.   Very often we are content with 1.5.   When we have a sprayed concrete of 100 mm thickness we core a diameter of 50 mm, and we are compelled to cut the ends of the cores so as to remove the skin and some rock; we are then content with a ratio of only 1.5, and we can - with formulae - get an equivalent cylinder strength.   I would think that for the British Standard, which operates on cubes, a ratio of 1.0 as a ratio of length to diameter is all that is necessary, but to obtain a very good specimen of cut-in-place would require a ratio of perhaps 1.5.

I have written to Mr Humphries at the Concrete Society, suggesting that to core in a 100 mm diameter when the usual thickness of sprayed concrete, averaging towards 100 mm of thickness and seldom more, was unfortunate.   The whole present reliability of small-diameter coring has been questioned for concrete. Last year (1979) in Stockholm, there was a very interesting Spanish contribution on concrete coring.   The author demonstrated that the scatter of results was very great with 100 mm concrete cores as compared with those of 150 mm.   But it may not be the same with sprayed concrete which is often sprayed mortar. It is very seldom that the aggregate is above 10 mm, and a 50 mm diameter core would be well adapted to the quality control of sprayed concrete.

E F HUMPHRIES (G Maunsell & Partners, UK):   From memory, BS 1881 says
that the absolute minimum ratio of length to diameter of a core is 0.95.
Obviously if that ratio is 1.5 or greater, the more satisfactory it is,
particularly where, as Msr Poitevin says, the ends of the core need to be
cut off and then capped in order to get a satisfactory core for compression
testing.   I think this is desirable.   But of course circumstances vary.
It may not be possible to get the right ratio in cases where the thickness
of sprayed concrete is less.   It just cannot be helped.   In such cases
one would have to rely on the results as best one could.   They would not be
authoritative if the core length/diameter ratio was less than the 0.95 laid
down in the British Standard.

L J BELL (UK Pressure Concrete Ltd., UK):   The point that Msr Poitevin
made is quite valid.   This is really why we do our routine quality control
testing from test panels.   These are set up adjacent to the work.   In fact,
one will just shove one under the nozzleman's nose twice a day and say
"fill that", and it can be made to any thickness one wants, not necessarily
restricting it to the thickness of the work which is actually being carried out.
A core can then be taken of the diameter one wants to give a representative core,
but at the same time maintaining the required length to diameter ratio.

J CAISLEY (Sir Robert McAlpine & Sons Ltd., UK):   A point about patency.
It was said earlier that the term 'shotcrete' would be used to describe sprayed
concrete with a coarse aggregate of 10 mm or greater.   Yet there was a similar
reference to fibrous concrete with aggregate less than 10 mm.
There seems to be a difference in nomenclature as between countries.

L J BELL: Indeed there is.   There is even a difference between different
people in this country!   We are hoping to settle this, at least as far as
the UK is concerned, in the terms that Eric Humphries has described, calling
everything sprayed concrete, but if it must be given a name other than
sprayed concrete, then that with less than 10 mm aggregate is to be called
gunite and that with 10 mm and above is to be called shotcrete.   It will

probably confuse us all more than when we started spraying, but that is the way it has turned out.

H WALKER (Turner-Morris (Pty) Ltd., South Africa):   The principle of using a panel to establish a test sample is not really representative of the material that is being placed in the work, which is actually being built up in layers. It is like a piece of a wall, which is obviously much stronger than a test sample made by using a panel.

L J BELL: Sprayed concrete is placed in layers, as Eric Humphries has described, by a number of passes with a nozzle over the area of the work. Naturally, the same technique would be used in constructing a test panel. The nozzle would not just be held in one place to construct a good test panel. The nozzle would have to be played over the area of that panel in a random pattern to build up the thickness required.   Then it really would be representative of the work.

H WALKER: I am suggesting that the test panel will be built up all at once, whereas the actual in situ product will get one pass, with perhaps an hour elapsing before the second pass is made.

L J BELL: It depends on the thickness.   The general thickness of a test panel, as mentioned in the Specification, is 100 mm.   That would not be done in layers with a gap of time between the layers.   The whole thing would be blown in all at one time.

E F HUMPHRIES: The main work is done in passes in just the same way. As Larry Bell says, the spraying of a test panel should be exactly similar to the way the actual main work is being carried out.

L J BELL: The only unrepresentative concrete one would get would be in a rather unusual situation, where the work being carried out was a considerable thickness of sprayed concrete, but the test panel was restricted to 100 mm thick.   But that would be an unusual application.

E F HUMPHRIES: But the thickness does not have to be restricted.   We say a <u>minimum</u> of 100 mm.

L J BELL: Indeed.   We say a minimum of 100.   If, for instance, someone is applying sprayed concrete 200 mm overhead - to take an extreme case - he would make a 200 mm thick test panel, and he would have to apply that in layers just the same.   One can get over the difficulty that way.

S R ARNOLD (Royal Military College of Science, UK):   I speak in no way as an expert in sprayed concrete;   perhaps I am one of the people who needs to be convinced that sprayed concrete is a good technique. What we are faced with - let us be absolutely honest about this, and I am sure I am echoing the views of a number of those present, is that sprayed concrete has something of a cowboy image.   People working off planks stuck on oil drums, no goggles, cigarette out of the corner of the mouth. These are some of the images that one has.   I should like to question - it was mentioned earlier and the question has not been answered - what arrangements are made for the training of operatives.   Are they simply put on site to learn by experience, at somebody else's expense, or does the Association operate some formal training scheme?   Is this training scheme followed by any form of certification and skills assessment?   Here I speak as the Chairman of the City and Guilds of London Institute Examination Committee No.1 for Construction, which is the concrete subjects.   As far as I know, sprayed concrete does not enter into any of these, although some of the courses operated, such as the Concrete Practice Course, would be eminently suitable for operatives.   The City and Guilds itself has an excellent Assessment Board which can advise on skills assessment.   I am not talking of written examinations, but the assessment of skills on the job.

Also in education, wearing my other hat and talking at the university level, I should like to make a plea for more assistance.   We are talking about the spread of use of sprayed concrete.   What better than to get at the student while he is still at university.   Does one want films that talk

about pounds per square inch and are obviously made long before the Health
and Safety at Work Act, or should we not now be looking towards video
cassettes instead of this 16 mm film that always breaks down?   Most
colleges and universities, even primary schools these days, have VCR facilities.

On the testing side, again being somewhat controversial and a little
critical, I am still filled with a certain amount of horror when I hear
reference about core testing to British Standard 1881.   I would like to
know on what authority anyone tests cores these days to BS 1881.   The
amendment slip that was issued in 1979 makes it quite clear that the cores,
particularly the correction factors for shape and length to diameter ratio,
have been discredited long ago by research.   I should like to think that
people these days are actually using the Concrete Society Working Party
Report on core testing that was published some years ago;   certainly in the
interpretation of core results.   The authority for this is in fact
contained in the amendment to BS 1881.

Finally, a question on a paper to come: the correlation between the Pull
Out Tests and the Cube Tests at high strength.   It is unfair to bring this
in now, but I was concerned in supervising some of the project work which
investigated the Pull Out Test.   I am interested to hear about the Probe
Test.   This does sound a fascinating move for the future.   Certainly I
wonder whether the Pull Out Test and its unreliability at high strengths in
terms of correlation is a question of the unreliability of testing sawn
cubes at high-strength concrete.   Really, which is being tested, the Pull
Out Test or the Cube Test?

CHAIRMAN: G COTTAM (Marples Ridgway Limited, UK):   Perhaps Mr Bell might talk
about training - the first question.   What are we doing about training, if
anything?

L J BELL: Perhaps I could start from the very beginning.   If I could
take some of the points that Mr Arnold made in the order in which he made
them.

First, the reference to the 'cowboy image'.   From what we have seen today, and from what we shall see, there is a certain justification for what he said.   By now it will have been noted that the lack of use of safety equipment is not confined to any one company, or to any one process, or to any one use of the medium, or even to any one country.   We have seen that it has been very widespread.   I did mention in my introduction that up until now, we, the contractors, have been faced with a great problem.   You can take a horse to water but you cannot make him drink.   We are hoping that we can make use of the help that we have been given now to improve the standards of safety on sites.

I have found, from personal experience, that in spite of the sort of things that we see, we do in fact have a very low accident rate - perhaps I should find some wood to touch in case that all changes!   Perhaps it is because what we are doing appears so dangerous that in some ways, although the chaps do not appear to be quite as safety conscious as they should, they at least have it in their minds.   They now need this 'push over the hill' to get them to use the equipment that is provided.   The Health and Safety at Work Act has given us the power to do so, and we do hope that the Code of Practice for Safe Working, with which - as I mentioned earlier - we are now heavily involved, will bring that to a proper conclusion.

As far as training and certification is concerned, certainly traditionally the training was done at a site level.   I have never heard - in the UK - of a training school for gunite operatives.   A chap starts as a labourer, perhaps, and as such he would be working near the gunite or concrete spraying machine.   He would see how that worked.   After a suitable time he would, if he had any gumption in him, ask to have a go, and when he was sufficiently experienced, he would undertake the working of that machine off his own bat.

I have never heard of a formal training scheme in this country.

CHAIRMAN: Do they have any training schemes in Switzerland?

G HAAG (Aliva Ltd., UK):   No, we do not.   The only training scheme
that I know of is in the United States, where, from time to time, they
hold so-called 'shotcrete schools' which end in a certificate.   These
involve not only the technological aspects of concrete, but also fieldwork,
sampling, etc.   The guy gets some sort of a certificate that would qualify
him.   That is about the only scheme I know of, worldwide.

CHAIRMAN: Can we now go on to testing.   The question of BS 1881 was
brought up.

E F HUMPHRIES: I quoted just the number, but in the Specification we do
give the exact part of that British Standard which relates to testing.
The answer is that there is nothing one can do better than to core, compare
the cores, and test.   Perhaps later on some technique will be evolved --
Tim Ryan has illustrated in his paper a mould for spraying to get a length
of beam from which a cube could be cut.   Whether that process will
eventually come into use, and therefore one should be able to test cubes in
a similar way as we do for normal concrete, I do not know.   It remains to
be seen whether that idea will be adopted.

C ALBERTS (Stabilator AB, Sweden):   A question was asked about training
systems.   In our company, Stabilator, we have such a scheme, occupying
several weeks.   We have practical training and theoretical studies both for
the operators (workers) and for the foremen.   These are later followed up
on site.   The theoretical studies include basic knowledge of cement and
concrete as well as some important facts about rock behaviour.
Now to my question.

It is said in the Proceedings that fibre reinforcement can be used together
with the "Challenge" machine.   Can Dr Littlejohn provide some information on
practical experience, on the limitations, on the volume of fibres and so on?

DR G S LITTLEJOHN (Colcrete Limited, UK):   I can only answer briefly.
I did not emphasize that the Challenge system is a recent introduction

into Britain, meaning of two years duration.   On wire-fibre reinforcement
we have followed - in our practice - the normal recommendations evolved in
the dry process.   We have never attempted, for example, to include more
than 2 per cent by volume of fibres.   That is not to say it could not be
done, but in our efforts to win co-operation with the consultant or the
client, we have agreed figures which have previously been published,
where it is known for a given percentage what improvements in flexural
strength will be attained.   We have not carried out development to
establish practical limits.   In other words, we have simply exploited
the use of fibres where the application has been suitable, using existing
technology.   Our main emphasis has been to try to win the co-operation of
clients in the use of the wet process.   I cannot answer the question
more fully at this time.

M. ADAM (U.T.I., France):   Most of the disorganizations of sprayed
concrete are due to heterogeneity of concrete around the reinforcement
bars corresponding with the shadow effect.   Looking at a cross section,
as shown by Dr Littlejohn, it appears to be correct, but spraying some
water on it, it is easy to note the differential behaviour of concrete
around the bars, part of the concrete remaining damp longer than the general
section.   I should like to know what can be done to avoid such
heterogeneity which leads to a poor durability of concrete when left in
severe weather conditions with the dry as well as with the wet method?

DR G S LITTLEJOHN: That is an extremely interesting question.
Whilst it is true that one can get lower quality material in the 'shadow'
area behind the reinforcement, given the correct cover and bearing in mind
that the reinforcement bars have an alkaline environment, I have never
encountered corrosion of the reinforcement locally where cracks have not
appeared from the outside through the cover.   In other words, with either
the dry or wet processes, there is no free water in the mix.   To suggest
that free water can create corrosion is absolutely valid, but if no free
water is encountered, how can corrosion be created?

Further, in conventional reinforced concrete, particularly with offshore
platforms, it has been our experience that if there is no feeding from the
outside of an aggressive water, but even if, say, there is some dampness,
that is self-passivating because of the alkaline environment.   It is only
when there is an ingress of water that can remove that alkalinity (depassivate)
and feed in fresh water that corrosion is promoted.   We have a fairly
simplistic view as structural engineers that, for the moment, whilst we know
no better, we must ensure good, dense and impermeable material with a
satisfactory cover which, generally speaking, should be not less than three
times the diameter of the reinforcement being protected.

M. ADAM: I have as an example of such behaviour the case of front masks
of earth dam with concrete sprayed as protection of the watertight screen –
Views Nos. 1 to 3.

DR G S LITTLEJOHN: Was that because of a shadow effect?

M. ADAM: Yes, I think so.

How would one avoid this shadow effect?   That is the problem.

Figure 1   General view of a front mask six years old
showing the importance of repairs and (arrow) the
facility to clean the reinforcement from concrete.

Figure 2 View of a cut slab of the mask which has been returned showing that underneath the bars the concrete is very poor (the dam was filled with a very pure water).

Figure 3 Detail of a damaged zone showing concrete fully disgregated under the bars, and above the bars the same concrete presenting a good behaviour.

DR G S LITTLEJOHN: The nozzle spraying technique has to be modified from the traditional normal to an inclined method in order to get full encapsulation of reinforcement. Bearing in mind that skill of the operator is still crucial to both the wet and dry processes, great care and perhaps reduction in output are required. If he did not work carefully, he would not get full encasement, and in a dam situation where there is a constant supply of slightly acidic water because it is pure, there can be a problem once it gets through the cover.

G HAAG: We had this problem with the dry mix as well, although it may be a little bit less critical because we were working with much dryer material originally, the water to cement ratio being very low.   But we would normally, in heavily reinforced areas, increase the operating pressure.   We are maintaining – generally – an operating pressure of between 3.5 and 4.0 kgs in order to avoid excessive dust formation and rebound, but in such cases, where we have to go through heavily reinforced areas, we would increase that to maybe 5.5 kgs, and the nozzle angle would have to be changed.   I quite agree with Dr Littlejohn that it is very much a matter of the experience of the nozzleman to avoid these shadows. We have not come across the phenomenon that has been described by Msr Adam.

PROFESSOR M VENUAT (CERILH, France):   On the subject of the dry process, in France we sometimes use a 'quick' cement with a setting time of about 3 minutes, but the aggregates must have less than about 3 per cent humidity.   A lot of work has been done in the past ten years with these types of cement in France, especially for tunnel lining, even where water will be coming in.   The colour of this cement is a light yellowish-brown, which is a very good colour in terms of the environment, especially for outside rock stabilization and for mortar rendering for housing.   For some purposes it is even possible to retard this with citric acid. Another way of obtaining a quick cement is to bind an alumina fondu cement with a portland cement.

Do the speakers have any experience of coloured sprayed concrete?

E F HUMPHRIES: I have heard that some contractors have added pigments to the dry mix before putting it into the machine, but I believe that the results thus obtained were not very good because there was a tremendous shadowing effect where the particles of sand from spraying in a particular area would drift on to the area that had just been sprayed.   Personally, I think that if someone wants coloured sprayed concrete, they can always put a coat of paint on it afterwards.   I cannot see the point in including a pigment in the whole thickness of a sprayed concrete application.

APPLICATIONS

I R S ROBERTSON (Binnie & Partners, UK): My question concerns the measurement of sprayed concrete in tunnels where the use of wire lines or timber profiles is not really on because of the difficult shapes in the tunnels. One would start with an agreed rebound factor and then work from there. The various methods I have come across are a given volume over a given area, minimum thickness on a high spot, putting in pegs at various intervals down the tunnel. Could the experts advise on any later or more ideal method of agreeing that the tunnelling is as required according to the Specification?

CHAIRMAN — J BENTLEY (E Gunite Limited): I am sure Eric Waller must have had ample experience of this problem at Dinorwic. Perhaps he would advise us how he got over it there.

E WALLER (James Williamson & Partners, UK): The designers were undecided as to where to use sprayed concrete or shuttered concrete in the various works. In three Busbar galleries it was decided to have a sprayed concrete arch built up in layers in order to improve the programme date in this particular area. We had Hilti bolts which were designed to hold fabric reinforcement in position, which in addition, in this case, formed depth gauges so that an arch of 150 mm thickness could be built up in 50 mm layers.

The type of contract used at the time at Dinorwic was the Target-Price contract; in it the initial layer of approximately 25 mm of sprayed concrete, usually with additive, was applied immediately after the rock had been exposed and prevented it dilating; this amount of sprayed concrete was paid for on a volume basis. The second layer, without additive, which was applied some time later, built up the lining to 50 mm or 75 mm whatever the Specification required; this was paid for on a square metre basis.

I would like to comment on the question raised on workmanship;
sprayed concrete cores were taken to monitor the skill of the
operatives which is vitally important with the turnover of labour which
is usual on a construction site.   I fully agree with what has been
said in that only experienced nozzlemen should be employed; and this
was the purpose, along with other factors, of the core examination.
The operatives were aware that the tests were being made and records
kept, the Contractor was able to trace the workmen who had carried out
the sprayed concrete at the location of the core, and from an
examination of it the Engineer was able to form an opinion of the work done.

T F RYAN (Theta Design Partnership, UK):   There are two choices:
one pays through the nozzle, including rebound, when one wants gunite
placed straight after the tunnelling machine, after the blast; this is
the only satisfactory way to overcome the problem.   Alternatively, when
it comes to placing the more permanent lining, it can be measured on the
square metre basis.

W B LONG (Whitley, Moran & Co Ltd., UK):   It is a serious problem.
Very often engineers or clients like to have the best of both worlds.
They want to pay for the least and get the contractor to put on the most.
We shall shortly be doing a small job for spraying on to a rock face,
where it has proved quite impossible to get the engineer to define what
he really wants.   The job is small, so it will not make a lot of
difference to us, but it is impossible to measure the volume that has
to be placed on the rock face.   In the end, more will be spent on
Hilti pins if they are put in a close enough spacing than on extra concrete.
I think one should probably pay on what goes through the nozzle.
Obviously one would have to monitor that the contractor is doing the work
to a reasonable standard and is not wasting an unreasonable amount of
material in rebound or in other ways.

DR G S LITTLEJOHN: I want to add a rider to a very good question.

It is still a problem in practice, even when we agree, as seems to be the trend, to measure through the nozzle for a flash coat, and then per square metre for the final lining.   The specialist subcontractor then gets into a terrible conflicting position between the client or the client's representative, and the main contractor, because of the overbreak.   The client or the consultant normally allows the main contractor a certain percentage overbreak.   He is then quite right in saying he wants the gunite contractor to spray 75 mm, and if he takes his final profile of the tunnel, he gets the total square metres, multiplies that by 75 mm, and everybody is happy except the specialist contractor, because he knows more concrete has been sprayed than is indicated by that volume.   In such a case the specialist has great difficulty in persuading the main contractor that a larger volume has gone on and that he should pay for the concrete.   This usually resolves itself by a specialist having to survey the tunnel perimeter at given sections, or by taking note of particular serious overbreak regions and bringing these to the attention of the consultant to get his agreement which, in turn, undermines the main contractor's position.   But it is a contentious subject in reality, even where the two bases for measurement have been logically agreed.

P POITEVIN:

A short comment on the limitations of sprayed concrete.   I believe that sprayed concrete, including gunite, is better than poured concrete, but it has its limitations.   This morning, Msr Adam alluded to the shadow effect behind the reinforcement, but there is a more general effect.   The strength of the concrete is proportional to the cement content of the mix, to the water content and to the void content.   For a very good concrete, with a water ratio of 0.5 - as was alluded to earlier for gunite - then for 360 kgs cement per m^3 we have about 145 l of water with voids.   A very good concrete will have a void content of perhaps 20 l/m^3, but in a sprayed mortar there will perhaps be 200 l/m^3.

One of the papers in this session said that the unit weight of gunite for sprayed concrete was 2 000 kgs/m^3, which is a void content in hardened sprayed concrete of about 20 per cent.   In good concrete it is 10 per cent.   Thus, from the point of view of durability, and especially the corrosion of reinforcement, there is a general lack of protection.   But it is corrected by the high cement content of sprayed concrete and generally further protection is not necessary.

In France, we generally use sprayed concrete - tunnelling by the Austrian Method - to support rock.   The sprayed concrete is only a temporary support for temporary work.   We use mesh in order to have a temporary support for the concrete, and the reinforcing effect is neglected.   But for permanent structures, such as the structures referred to in the papers, which had to be strengthened, these were excellent examples where such strengthening was used.   For old structures, it is better to strengthen with good gunite than with nothing.   But for new structures it can be questionned.   In dams and similar structures it has its limitations, particularly where sensitive reinforcement like stressed bars and prestressed concrete are used.   A well known American process is to build water tanks using sprayed concrete in order to protect the prestressing wires.

We all know of the New York collapse of some such tanks.   In France, too, we had a similar unfortunate experience involving a 6 m diameter water pipe built above ground.   It was in the mountains, to carry water from the Dordogne. It was prestressed, using external wires, stressed by the winding process, and protected by a 100 mm layer of sprayed concrete.   It was then covered with earth, so as to minimize thermal effects.   The environment was damp, and the concrete was always damp, with water within and without, and several years after it was built, it collapsed.   The collapse was investigated, and it was concluded that it was not a good practice to use sprayed concrete and to cover it with earth.   It was also found that the sprayed concrete on top of the pipe was very poor because rebound had been integrated with the sound concrete and, in fact, the major fracture occurred in this section.   In consequence, in France we now never protect prestressing tendons in pipes or in tanks with sprayed concrete.   We use it only in tunnels, and from time to time in strengthening old reinforced concrete work.

H WALKER: I was interested in the numerous applications we have
been shown in the housebuilding field.   Have there ever been any developments
in the coal-mining industry, for stoppings?   Could this be explained?
We have done a lot of experimentation with few results.   We tried a cardboard
panel once but we had problems with fire resistance and it could not be
accepted.

T F RYAN: I have not had too much experience in coalmines myself,
but there is someone here who could give quite a background on stoppings.

DR G S LITTLEJOHN: It is a problem we have looked at from the point of view
of spraying concrete, but there is a problem because on occasions there tends
to be sparking caused by rebound between aggregate particles.   In Britain
there are about seventy collieries which suffer spontaneous combustion, and in
these mines, a different approach has been taken based on grouting.   When
roadways are being supported, or long-wall faces are being advanced, the most
common system currently being developed to move away from the traditional pack
systems where blocks of wood or waste are employed, is now to use flexible fabric
bags which are positioned immediately behind the hydraulic jacks, for example,
and these flexible fabric bags are grouted up.   They are self-inflating, the
fabric is fireproof, and a very rapid-setting grout which goes hard within
twenty minutes is injected.   That minimises roof convergence as well as creating
a fire barrier protecting the roadway from the void behind.   That is currently
under development in some half-a-dozen mines.   If it is accepted, then after a
year or two it may become a common technique.   It looks full of promise since
it is a cheap and rapid method of support.   It can keep up with the highest
production rates of the advancing faces and it is very simple.   Gunite has not
been applied in the main for such applications although it can offer a
satisfactory lining in suitable circumstances.

CHAIRMAN: Mr Long wants to reply to Msr Poitevin's comments
in the earlier discussion on the French technique.

104

W B LONG: Two points.

A question was asked in Session I about the use of colouring agents in gunite.
We have had two experiences of the use of colouring agents.   In one case,
where we were asked to gunite the exterior of a steel chimney for camouflage
reasons on a Ministry establishment, this was done in gunite incorporating a
green colouring agent.   The whole thickness was done in green because they did
not want the risk of a surface coating wearing off.   It is still green after
twenty years, and the colouring agent cost more than the cement.

We had another instance of using a brown colouring agent in gunite in a
National Park where they wanted to make it look a bit more like stone.   I think
it looks like brown gunite.

Secondly, I wanted to take issue with Msr Poitevin.   With due respect to our
guests, and the entente cordiale, I do not believe that gunite is a bad protector
of steel.   I have not seen nor have been given any evidence to that effect.
There are bad jobs, there are bad instances, but the densities we usually get in
gunite are about 2 250 kgs/m^3.   I do not know what void ratio this is but in my
opinion it is a good quality concrete, providing good protection to steel.
Tim Ryan showed a number of examples, and there are many others, of new reinforced
concrete structures built with sprayed concrete, and there is no evidence that
they are likely to corrode rapidly or to fall down.   I feel there may have
been some other factor in the French instance quoted.

There have certainly been large numbers of prestressed tanks done in this country,
externally prestressed, where the prestressing wires are protected with gunite.

I am sure that gunite provides good long-term protection to steel, and that the
use of gunite could in no way lead, and there is no general evidence that it would
lead, to early breakdown.

H BLAKEY (John Laing R & D Ltd., UK): To follow up on the protection of
the steel, and regarding the slides that were shown of guniting in hot,
dry climates.   Were there any problems in application there, and what

steps had to be taken, if any, on the curing of such concrete, which is
drying out extremely rapidly even when it is freshly placed?   I wonder about
the permeability and long-term durability of gunite concrete in that
situation?

T F RYAN: When we started to spray concrete in a structural manner in
hot climates, we did not have too much to guide us apart from some of the
American practice and we had to feel our way.   We had a pretty good idea of
what was likely to damage the concrete.   As I pointed out in the paper, we
endeavoured to limit our working hours.   We did not work in the heat of the
day.   We found that the most damaging thing was not the sun; it was the
wind.   It was the wind running over the surface that was the real trouble.
So we made sure to keep the wind off the work, and we did as much wet-curing
as we possibly could.   One of the good things about working in the Middle East
is that there may not be many expert workmen around, but there are a lot of
guys who can throw water.   All that one needs is the water.   That is
largely our attitude.

N M AABIDI (Gulf & Jordan, Jordan):   In making thin elements by guniting,
there is always a problem of cracks in some arid areas where there is quite
a variation in temperature between night and day, and between summer and winter.
What is the best approach for dealing with such a phenomenon?   Is it adding
certain additives, or spraying in a certain way?   What is the most effective
way to avoid such cracks?

T F RYAN: One of the things that we decided in the very early days
was not to use wet mix systems in hot climates, but to use dry mix.   This
meant that we could keep the water:cement ratio down as far as possible.
There are no two ways about it.   If the water:cement ratio can be kept down,
then the shrinkage which tends to generate those cracks that eventually open
up does not occur.   Gunite has the saving ability of a very high cement
content.   We found that much of the cracking that was pointed out to us

was only surface cracking.   It did not penetrate to any great depth, largely because the cement content curing over a longer period of time than normal had taken up the cracks and only left the traces.   We did not have - we still have not had - any problems with cracking in any of our structures in the Middle East.

W B LONG: One needs to distinguish between cracking and surface crazing.   Gunite is very susceptible to surface crazing, but this is a shallow effect.   It is not structural, even if it does not look very good.   If cracking right through the structure is occurring, then arguably the wrong reinforcement is in the wrong place.   There should be enough reinforcement, and the positioning of the joints should be such, that actual cracking through the structure does not occur.

T F RYAN: A number of things crop up in terms of working with materials in the Middle East.   One is that the sands that are available have to be used. In the early days, we found that the sands tended to be crushed local rock, and they had an enormous quantity of fines.   The fines, apart from anything else, tend to increase the water:cement ratio, and they tend to contain nearly all the impurities that we wanted to be rid of, so we did our utmost to eliminate the fines as much as possible.   Nowadays much better sands are available throughout most of the Middle East, largely due to many, many contractors demanding better sands and getting them, so the problem does not now arise.

One of the other problems is the reinforcement itself.   If cracking occurs, often it is the state that the reinforcement was in before starting to apply the concrete.   That is very much the case with gunite.   The reinforcement tends to be left, and in a marine environment there will be a certain amount of salt deposition on the reinforcement, and it just has to be kept clean. It is fortunate that the dry mix gun is a piece of equipment that is extremely able to clean that reinforcement.   If a wet sand blast is put through the machine before starting spraying, that reinforcement is really ripped, then the steel will be absolutely clean and naked.   That is what we do.

W B LONG: I should like to ask Eric Waller one further point on the testing he mentioned earlier, when he referred to the Hilti equipment. Has he done any correlation tests between the Hilti equipment and any other testing methods to show that he is getting reliable results?   Is it a continuing number of site trials, or what?

E WALLER: This trial was done for our military colleagues at Shrivenham.   One of our Partners' sons was there, and thought it to be good training for him to develop this particular subject, the strength testing of sprayed concrete.   It was developed - as described in the paper - solely with Hilti studs; and the study was carried out over a limited period of time. Further work needs to be done.   Dr Littlejohn stated that work on the in-situ testing of sprayed concrete is being done in several quarters; I look forward with keen interest to the results.

W B LONG: So that in fact will be another means, rather like the Windsor Probe, to attain the end result.

E WALLER: I think it is akin to that.

S R ARNOLD: The student concerned did excellent work.   As an ordinary student, it was quite an outstanding project.   I should like to support that and to say that there is a lot of work still to be done in this field.   I wonder whether it is being taken any further.   It was remarkably cheap, incredibly quick, and very simple.   It works on a similar principle to the Windsor Probe, but we could never determine how it works in theory.   In practice it gave a very good correlation.

One thing I wondered earlier on, when we were talking about cores, was correlation.   The problem of correlation is that the core is being tested against something that is itself uncertain.   One is not quite sure.   If the pullout test is tested against cores, or something of that nature, then is it the Hilti Probe or the Windsor Probe that is giving the right answer, and the core that is giving the wrong answer?   This is one of the problems.

I should also like to come back briefly and have a second bite of the cherry. In no way was I trying to get at the Association of Gunite Contractors earlier on. What I was stating is a matter of fact. There is something about sprayed concrete that has about it a mystique, an art. Very little an engineer can say when putting something in a planning application; "Well, I have done all the calculations; here you are; it will stand up; these are the men and they will be doing this", and there is this certain mystique about it. I did suggest certain things that I thought could be done to improve the situation. For example, the standard method of training supervisors is through the City & Guilds supervisory courses. Is there anything on sprayed concrete in the syllabus? If it is put in the syllabus, the teacher will teach it. More people will get to know about sprayed concrete and the whole thing will spread. I mentioned earlier the facilities for getting at people young, at universities, and providing quick simple aids in which lecturers like myself can show students something of what we have seen today; what sprayed concrete is, what its possibilities are and what its potentials are. I am making a plea for something of a PR exercise, education in the broadest sense. I still feel that, for example, the Cement and Concrete Association could lay on training courses at the operative level. I accept fully that on-site training is possibly the best way for the UK compared with America. But would it not be possible to give a person who is recognised in any individual firm some form of certification, something that he can hold in his hand and say: "I am recognised by my employer as being a skilled man. He has told me that he thinks well of me and this is my certificate to prove it"? That is what I mean by certification. This would be just one way that could help.

Finally, I am surprised, still, that under the Federation of Civil Engineering Contractors National Working Rule Agreement, the only recognised trade is that of leveller and screeder. There is no such thing as concretor, and many of the other modern skills are totally omitted. This again detracts from the status, and perhaps someone down there is a gunitor, or gunite operator. Recognition. This is what it is all about.

W B LONG: I would comment as one who, with a number of others present,
was very much involved in forming the Association of Gunite Contractors, and
who had the honour to be their first Chairman.   What we were attempting to
do was to remove the mystique and to lay our experience on the table, to try
and make available all the knowledge that had been gained over the years.
It is very true that in the past a number of companies were totally unwilling
to make available their experience because they regarded it as their commercial
'knowhow'.   This was their goodwill.   This was what they had to hold tight
to their chest.   I think we have moved a step in the right direction.

There has always been a reluctance in this country to give people
classifications, and pay people extra money on account of those classifications,
and then to find that no one but this man can be employed in that
classification, so then there would be all sorts of demarcation problems.
The Federation of Civil Engineering Contractors is very conservative in this
respect - and I sit on a Section Committee.   For us to move quicker than the
Federation would be a difficult thing to do, but I take the point.   We, in
the Association, should do everything and will do everything, to look into
the feasibility of this.   In recent years we have certainly shown that we
are very happy to provide speakers at seminars, meetings and conferences, and
we would provide speakers at universities or anywhere else to give a short
talk on a particular aspect, some rather specialist aspect, which probably
cannot be dealt with adequately by a general lecturer, however good or willing,
because he does not have the experience.

P POITEVIN: The answer to Mr Long is to quote him and to say that guniting
is an art.   But there are poor practitioners.

One question to which I did not allude.   Formerly it was usual to include
calcium chloride in admixtures, and in some cases the corrosion of the
reinforcement was due to such admixtures.

W B LONG: Perhaps I must speak as one artist to another!   Generally speaking, admixtures and accelerators would not be used in guniting, except in particular cases. 99% of normal work carried out does not incorporate an accelerator. There is a major problem with accelerators and admixtures of which we are all aware - the variability of dosage. This is where the main problems have occurred with calcium chloride. It is bad anyway, and it is terrible with an overdosage.

Do they sell calcium chloride now? I suppose it is not sold. Much better admixtures that do not have this harmful effect are available. I would say for a start, never use calcium chloride, and it is probably rarely used today.

W A BARBER (Brown & Root (UK) Ltd., UK): I should like to ask three questions:-

(1) In the case of repairing concrete, what is the basis
     for determining the depth of cutback?

(2) What tests are used to ascertain the bond between the
     gunite applied and the original concrete?

(3) Could we also have some indication of comparative
     costs on the wet and dry processes?

I appreciate there are certain areas where a wet process might be more desirable than the dry, and vice versa, but it may be that in the middle ground there is some comparative trade-off for costs which one could use in evaluation for the process to be adopted.

DR G S LITTLEJOHN: To take the last two points. In relationship to the costs between the wet and the dry process, it is 'horses for courses'. The wet process is generally used on large-scale applications where the cost per cu.m placed comes out cheaper than the dry process. In general, the dry process would be preferred on thin or small structural sections, where the cost per square metre comes out more beneficial than cast concrete, but in that situation it would not be competing against the wet mix system which could not be applied.

In respect of the bond, we saw a slide of Eric Waller's taken at Dinorwic showing the adhesion of the gunite to the slate and the way that it was integrated into it, indicating the type of bond which can be attained - almost a mechanical interlock. Good bond is dependent upon good surface preparation and in such circumstances failure invariably occurs in the weaker parent material and not at the interface. Where interface failure has been recorded for smooth paving slabs shot with gunite adhesions have ranged from $0.98 - 1.68$ N/mm^2 for 35N/mm^2 gunite. There is one test, a Pull Out Test, which some consultants still specify for checking the adhesion. In Tim Ryan's book there is a detail of the Pull Out Test and it has certainly been used in recent times.

W A BARBER: The determination of the extent of cutting back, so as to make the decision that we have actually gone back far enough.

DR G S LITTLEJOHN: In the repair situation, I think that the Concrete Society's Code of Practice has set out what is realistic, generally, i.e., not to cut out behind the centre line of the bar. I am talking of UK practice where questions of guniting technique and shadow effect are taken into consideration. The other aspect is not to cut out good concrete which is pointless.

W B LONG: There are two separate considerations here. If calcium chloride is present, then one has to cut away and expose the steel reinforcement. This is a particular situation, and with deterioration due to the presence of an excess of calcium chloride, one must cut right back. Of course the structure will be damaged in doing so. Probably the dead load will have to be supported, and live load kept off.

In an ordinary repair context, it is only necessary to cut away unsound concrete to get back to sound material at whatever depth that happens to be found. It is not specifically necessary to cut out to half the depth of the steel, or behind the depth of the steel, or anywhere else but only to get back to sound material.

112

Someone will now ask how one knows when one has done that. There is no straight answer to that, except that sound material is very hard to cut out, so that when it becomes very hard going, enough has been cut out.

T F RYAN: In terms of the adhesion of the gunite to the concrete, Bill Monks at the C & CA did some work in terms of actually applying areas of gunite to lumps of concrete and trying to haul them off. The results he discovered were quite interesting. He found that if the surface was grit-blasted and dry, the adhesion was higher. The difficulty is that a dry surface cannot normally be found when spraying with gunite. Normally the surface has been washed over. Even so, he did have some figures which gave a range of values for normal concrete surfaces to which gunite is applied for a pull off value.

Various other research departments for major contractors like, I believe, Taylor Woodrow and Wimpeys, have done some work. They have got figures which they use in calculations, and they will probably make those available in the long term.

CHAIRMAN: I should like to leave the subject with a few comments that I have noted during the day.

First, the advantages of using gunite, sprayed concrete.   I shall read from our Association's leaflet. It is quite pertinent.

> "The advantages to the designers of specifying gunite or shotcrete
> are: high strength, dense, homogeneous concrete is obtained;
> reduction or elimination of shuttering costs and constraints;
> free form designs can be used; work is carried out at high speed,
> relatively; cost reductions through higher outputs on large areas
> and thin sections are obtainable; exotic shapes and finishes can
> be achieved; thin shells or sections are very economically formed,
> and difficult access problems are all so easily coped with........".

Some things to bear in mind!

And now a point from Eric Humphries's presentation. He said: "Get yourself a good contractor; get yourself a good specification;   combine one with the other and you should get good gunite".   I think that is a very pertinent point.

Errata (in 'CI80 Sprayed Concrete' – E F Humphries)

References 6 and 10 on page 15 are amended as follows:

6.   The Concrete Society   (1980)   "Code of Practice for
                                                Sprayed Concrete".
                                                Ref. 53.030.

10.   Swedish Concrete   (1973)   "Specification for Concrete
      Committee   Structures, Materials and
                                               Code of Practice regarding
                                               Concrete".
                                               Publication B5 Chapter 4.

Fibrous concrete

Applications of glass fibre reinforced concrete in Rumania

M Hamalgiu and D Constantinuscu
Research and Design Institute for Building Materials Industry, Rumania

The multiple advantages the new material "GRC" presents have drawn the attention of the Romanian specialists who investigate and test it for very different construction elements. There were appreciated both the possibility of achieving supple, high quality precast elements in a large diversity of forms and with a reduced wall thickness (6-15 mm) which leads to a smaller weight of the construction elements and the fact that the steel consumption is reduced to a minimum one, at the same time obtaining a high impact strength as compared to asbestos cement.

As the "GRC"is however a new material which has not reached yet a decade since England has introduced it in the market and due to the insufficient experimental data available on its time behaviour in various working, climatic and environmental conditions, the investigations, the experiments and the achievements in Romania were firstly guided to the non-structural construction elements.

But parallel with the introduction of the GRC products for non-structural elements, The Research and Design Institute for Building Materials Industry (ICPMC) in Bucharest has also approached the investigations and testing of some structural elements. Submitted to long duration tests these could give an answer to the utilization of GRC in this field too, where the advantages of the new material could present an even greater interest both technically and economically.

By using an adequate equipment for the preparation and placement of GRC as well as a suitable technology for vacuum treatment of fresh mortar together with a new conception of making up the moulds, a series of non-structural products have been achieved, they comprising a wide range of utilizations in constructions such as:

1. Sanitary mask (fig. 1) used for covering the plumbing to the bath rooms.

2. Ventilating tube (fig. 2) used in dwelling buildings.

3. Thermal insulating panels mounted on the outer concrete walls (fig. 3).

4. Corrugated plates for closings (particularly – for roofs) – (fig. 4).

5. Balcony railings (fig. 5).

6. Partition wall made up of strips for inner partitionings (fig. 6).

7. Thermal insulating panel in a very light structure conception (fig. 7)

8. Curtain – wall panel with embedded windows (fig. 8)

9. Centrifuged pipes of 5.0 m in length (fig. 9)

10. Prefab bath rooms (fig. 10)

Some of the investigated and tested products have been introduced into the mass production on a technological line of a high degree of mechanization (fig. 11 and 12)

Parallel with the manufacture of non-structural elements made out of GRC there were conceived, designed, investigated and tested some series of structural elements for use as roofing elements for industrial constructions. Thus there were produced and tested thermal insulating roof elements of 0.60 cm in width and of 3.0, 6.0, 9.0 and 12.0 m in length (fig. 13 and 14).

All the tested roof elements have a cross section of a rectangular shape, the wall thickness varying from 0.8 – 1.5 cm depending on the element length (fig. 15).

The reduced net weight of these elements (40 – 70 kgf/sq.m) and the important steel saving resulting from the assembly design of a structure using a light roof made out of GRC strips made the attention be focussed on solving these structural elements.

In manufacture of all these elements a special technology was used which gave the possibility of obtaining very good results on concrete specimens tested for bending stress (fig. 16); the strengths varied between 320 – 400 daN/sq.cm to an average content of 5% CEM-FIL fibre.

All the roof elements, calculated for a working load of 120 kgf/sq.m (snow + hydrofuge insulation) had a suitable behaviour to the bending stress while for the ultimate load the registered safety coefficients varied from 2.8 to 5.1.

Fig. 17 shows the testing of the 12.0 m long roof element. The test was carried out with the load evenly distributed by means of tanks successively filled with water.

The loads have been applied in three stages as follows:

- Ist stage – from 0 – to – 135 kgf/sq. m to 0
- IInd stage – from 0 – to – 297 kgf/sq. m to 0
- IIIrd stage – from 0 – to – 486 kgf/sq. m

Fig. 18 illustrates the diagram of the deflections measured at the strip center, it indicating that the removal of the load does not significantly affect the deflection curve which marks a continous evolution.

It should be noted that no crack in the lower part of the element was seen up to the ultimate load while failure took place in the compressed zone because of a local error placed in the upper plate of the section.

It has been found that, within the measurements efected and as regards the variation of the specific strains in 67 positions both in the compressed zone and in the tensioning one of the 12.0 m strip, the values are correlated with the charges and have a normal evolution without registering any particular phenomenon.

The values in the table below resulted from the graphic recordings carried out by means of the strain registering meters at the middle of the beam.

Maximum strain		loading in kgf/sq.m	
		135	465
Compressed zone	mm/meter	0.2	1.0
Tensioning zone		0.16	1.5

The experiments also proved that the GRC strips submitted to a long duration loading (2 - 3 years) (fig. 19 and 20) distort continuously, the deflections highly increase and in many cases, the influence of the creep may represent a decisive criterion for the design of these elements. Thus, with the 3.0 m strips, the curve of time-strains under the action of a constant load of 120 kgf/sq. m is as in fig. 21 from which results that, after 8 - 10 months, the curve increment is no more significant.

With the 6.0 and 9.0 m strips - after 18 months - the deflections continue to increase which will make the design elements be reconsidered by taking into consideration all the factors contributing to the creep of concrete.

In the first stage the 3.0 m strips are to be used for roofing an experimental construction, this time being checked in constructions the way of behaviour in a structure over a period of several years.

The investigations and the experiments will be continued both for finalizing some official design instructions for the structural elements made out of GRC and for achieving new types of GRC elements with a span of up to 18.0 m.

Figure 1.

Figure 2.

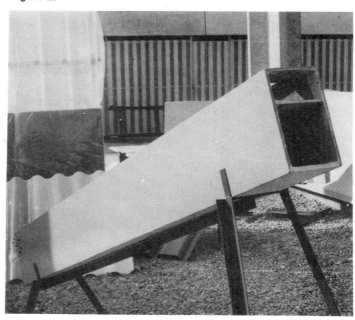

Figure 3.

Figure 4.

Figure 5.

Figure 7.

Figure 8.

Figure 6.

Figure 9.

Figure 10.

Figure 11.

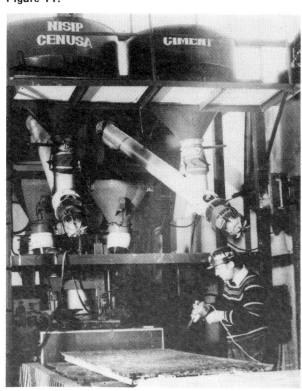

Figure 12.

Figure 13.

Figure 14.

Figure 15.

Figure 16.

Figure 17.

Figure 18.

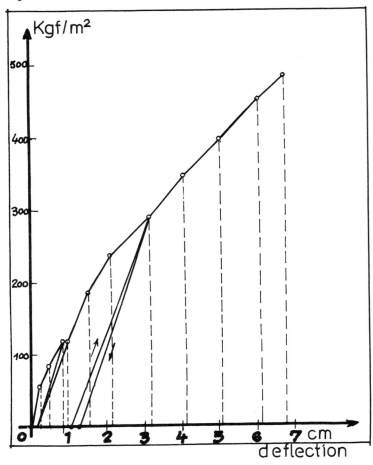

Figure 19.

Figure 20.

Figure 21.

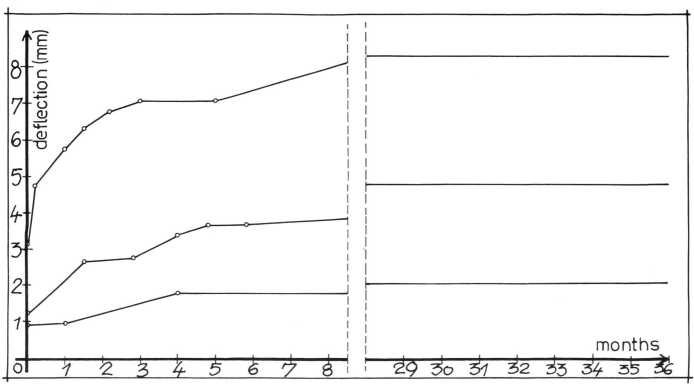

General discussion

MATERIALS AND PERFORMANCE

DR C D POMEROY (Cement and Concrete Association, UK):
One question that I should like to ask all the speakers is what, from
the user's point of view, do we want in terms of the useful energy that
fibre concrete can absorb.   At one extreme, fibre concrete can be used
to stop explosives.   If we have explosives and we want to contain an
explosion, we do not mind if the building should look broken and cracked
afterwards provided that it has fulfilled its function.   On the other hand,
if a thin sheet of fibrous material is deformed to a grid catenary this may
well not be acceptable to the user, but the sheet is still structurally sound.
Therefore, when we are talking about energy absorption, impact resistance, and
ability to contain cracking as advantageous characteristics of fibre concrete,
I would like the speakers' views on how much of this can we really use.

K D RAITHBY (Bridge Design Division, Transport & Road Research Laboratory, UK):
I refer to Mr Henager's paper, particularly with regard to the standardization
of testing in relation to the type of testing machine used.   Various
mechanically operated and hydraulically operated machines were described and
some mention was made of differences in behaviour of the composites according
to whether strain or load is controlled.   When measuring energy absorption in a
standard test it is important to define the mode of control.   In my opinion a
controlled rate of strain or displacement is essential for this type of testing
and needs to be specified in particular numerical terms.

C H HENAGER (Battelle Pacific Northwest Laboratories, USA):

In a paper I presented at the RILEM Symposium at Sheffield in 1978, I did specify that the rate of deformation should be the controlling factor in toughness testing. However, in the publication of the work by the American Concrete Institute, this particular factor has been left out, so that it needs to be specified that rate of deformation should be controlled, and not rate of loading.

H KRENCHEL (Structural Research Laboratory, Technical University of Denmark, Denmark):

I shall try to give an answer to a previous questioner, because I think that he asked one of the most essential questions of all. If I might rephrase the question, I would say how much extensibility, or how much improvement of the ultimate straining capacity of a brittle material is needed? How much fibre will have to be put in, and in which way?

If we take neat cement, which is the basic material in asbestos cement, we find, as Dr Hannant showed on one of his first slides, that the strain capacity in tension is about 0.5 per mil (500 microstrain). If a block of this material is drying out from the outside, the shrinkage is about four to five times as much as the ultimate strain capacity with the result, naturally, that the outside layers of the material are restrained from shrinking and the material starts cracking. The cracks might be rather small but such cracks in the brittle material will always start the deterioration of the material later on. In theory we could say if by means of the fibres we can improve the strain capacity of the material so that it is bigger than the drying shrinkage, we shall have - in my opinion - a sound material. In order to have a sound material that will not lose strength when drying out and that will not deteriorate later on, the strain capacity must be somewhat more than the total drying shrinkage.

G G MADELEY (Don Fibres Limited, Scotland, UK):

I am concerned that polypropylene may be criticized for its performance under external weathering conditions. As manufacturers of polypropylene tapes, yarns and fibres, we are aware of the problems of ultra-violet degradation, but we have many techniques for stabilising these products. In fact, to quote an extreme case, it is now possible to put synthetic grass carpets made from polypropylene outdoors in parts of the world such as Saudi Arabia where they will last for at least two years. Have any durability studies been carried out using stabilized polypropylene in concrete?

DR D J HANNANT (University of Surrey, UK): I am not a polymer chemist and I know very little about the ultra-violet stability of polypropylene. The argument usually used is that when polypropylene is placed within concrete, even at a very shallow depth, there is no penetration of ultra-violet to the polypropylene, so that it does not degrade. In order to check this prediction, we are carrying out durability tests on stabilised polypropylene films in cement.
Perhaps a polymer chemist who is familiar with factors affecting the degradation of polypropylene would care to make some additional comments.

D G ELLIS (Plasticisers Limited, UK): In our experience as a leading European polypropylene fibre manufacturer, with specialist grades for reinforcement applications, it is clear that u.v. degradation can if necessary be controlled by the incorporation of suitable stabilizers in the polypropylene. However, the addition of suitable antioxidants to polypropylene is more important than u.v. stabilizers. As Dr Hannant noted previously, the screening effect of the cement can limit the transmission of light, but cement is sufficiently porous to require polypropylene to be protected against oxidation, and this can be done in commercially available polypropylenes.

M J N JACOBS (DSM, Research and Patents, The Netherlands):
I would like to comment on one of Dr Majumdar's figures (figure 8) in which data is shown on a direct tensile curve for a polymer modified mortar.
I found it surprising that he should give a deformation of less than 1 per mil (1000 microstrain) at break at a strength of 12 MPa which would indicate a tangent modulus of at least 12 GPa. From the slope of the curve, I would

judge the initial modulus to be perhaps around 20 GPa, which is an unusually high tangent modulus for a polymer modified mortar.

Secondly, I refer to the remark about the mechanism of ageing of materials. We have been thinking for many years about the deterioration of the fibres, but as Dr Majumdar showed, and as was clear from some of his graphs, there are other mechanisms that are quite important. The mechanism that I want to stress here is that there is an apparently increasing bond with the course of time between matrix and fibres. I would suggest in this case - as can be seen by the decreasing strains at break - that the brittleness is caused in the system by increasing bond so that the control of the bond strength, that is of the shear bond strength between the fibre and the matrix, is of prime importance for the control of the ductile properties of the material.

DR A J MAJUMDAR: (D.O.E. Building Research Establishment, UK):
I would agree on the second point. It is a question of whether one has measured values of bond strength, and shear strength, to make a quantitative assessment of the effects on the stress-strain curve. One knows that the bond strength must increase, but looking in the literature there is very little in the way of values which will allow one to say that <u>this</u> is the increase in shear bond strength so that the results can be quantitatively explained.
OPC/grc without any added polymer gives an initial Young's modulus value in the range 25-32 GPa after 5 years of natural weathering. Polymer loading in the case cited was low, at 10% polymer solids, and therefore 20 GPa as the value for the Young's modulus does not seem improbable. For the high UTS value we have no explanation at the present moment.

DR P SULLIVAN (Imperial College, London, UK): Mr Proctor mentioned that he uses a temperature coefficient for extrapolation. Could he enlarge on that coefficient? Figure 2, which shows deterioration of MOR with time, has been plotted on a log time scale. The rate of reduction is therefore exaggerated and makes the material appear much worse than it actually is. Has he perhaps also plotted this graph on a normal basis to show a more realistic decrease in MOR?

B A PROCTOR (Pilkington Brothers Limited, UK): Taking the last part first. We have also plotted time on a linear axis, and it does show, as Dr Sullivan suggests, that rate of loss of strength is decreasing steadily. The log plot does rather accentuate the falling strength condition. There are disadvantages, in a sense - psychological ones - in using a log plot, but it is a convenient way of compressing timescales as long as one remembers that it is a logarithmic plot, and that time is getting very much longer for an equivalent increment of distance along the X axis.

To return to the first part of the question. The way that we have arrived at the temperature coefficient is to produce an Arrhenius type plot. For instance, rate of loss of strength has been plotted against 1 over the absolute temperature and the linearity of this plot shows that this is a good Arrhenius relationship. Also the degree of extrapolation, from the range of experimental results that we have obtained to the sort of working temperatures that we wish to predict, is a relatively small amount compared with the total range of temperatures that we have looked at experimentally. Hence, we are not extrapolating very far on that Arrhenius relationship and we are not relying on its remaining linear for any greater length than we have actually investigated. We then relate, in terms of natural weather, to a temperature which is very close to the mean annual temperature of a given climate, and we find a very good correlation with different climates by doing that.

DESIGN, MANUFACTURE AND APPLICATIONS

D C HUGHES (University of Surrey, UK):
This question refers to Dr Krenchel's paper. I was very interested in the use of the frayed polypropylene fibres as a method of increasing the

fibre-matrix bond. Has Dr Krenchel done any work to optimize the amount of fraying that is necessary, and is there any significant increase in bonding efficiency if the fraying technique is used to increase the specific surface area compared with creating more surface area by the use of finer monofilament?

H KRENCHEL: I am sorry, but I did not understand the exact terms of the question. What I can say is that the fibre which I mentioned is frayed at the edges - as shown on the electron micrograph. It is also treated on the surface, in two ways, electrical treatment, and chemical treatment involving some kind of liquid being sprayed on it.

The stress/strain curves which I showed give - at least indirectly - some proof of the considerably improved bond. If stress/strain curves are drawn for ordinary cement materials reinforced with ordinary plastic fibres without these treatments, these will be the normal type of stress/strain curves, for example, as soon as the LOP is reached the material extends to failure with ordinary cracking, as shown in my Figure 11(2). I cannot give figures of the bond strength in MPa with these very small fibres because we have not been able to measure it, and in fact we are more interested in the indirect measurement showing how the composite works when the two components are put together in the right way.

DR P SULLIVAN (Imperial College, London, UK): Mr Hackman mentioned two castables; a hard cast, if I remember correctly, and a kiln cast. He mentioned that one was 160 lbs/cu.ft material, and the other was 130 lbs/cu.ft. Could he say what the matrix is? He also suggested that the kiln cast was one which had very high thermal cycling, and I was surprised to hear that large aggregates were being used in preference to small aggregates.

L E HACKMAN (Ribbon Technology Corporation, USA):
The materials were primarily high alumina castables. The aggregate size was approximately 3/4 to 1 inch (20 - 25 mm). Most of the castables have aggregate sizes down to 3/8ths inch (6 - 10 mm).

DR P SULLIVAN: Is the larger aggregate more resistant to thermal cycling than the smaller aggregate?

L E HACKMAN: It has been found that more strengthening is apparently given by the larger aggregates.   Ribbon Technology have nothing to do with the castable which is designed by the refractory company who have experience to show that to give better thermal cycling resistance a large aggregate is required.   It may be acting as a larger reinforcing member in the castable. Steel fibre will help that reinforcement even further, and longer steel fibre could help even more.   The fibre that was used in these tests was 1-inch (25 mm) long which is nearly the same size as the aggregate and cannot be expected to be as effective in strengthening a longer fibre.

G KAPKA (Department of Transport, UK):   What is the coefficient of thermal expansion of glass?   Is it the same as the concrete paste sorrounding it and, if it differs, by how much does it differ?   I already know that the coefficient of thermal expansion of the plastic materials, polypropylene and others, differs widely from the sand/cement grout.   How does Dr Krenchel propose to cope with this problem?   I also believe that the coefficient of thermal expansion of plastic materials changes with temperature itself.

L E HACKMAN: Working with high-temperature refractories and steel fibre, we get that same question many times.   In all the problems of fibre-reinforced concretes involving thermal coefficients of expansion, the major problems come when a continuous reinforcing member is used, and not when short members are used

Short members do not have the large accumulative expansion of a continuous member, thus do not result in forces that are high enough to create a problem within the matrix material.   Within the high-temperature applications, where we are using steel in the refractories, and we are going up to temperatures in the neighbourhood of 1200°C and then returning back to room temperature, we find no cracking and no adverse effects from thermal expansions. This is primarily because the fibres are very fine, they are short in length, and the forces that are applied to the matrix material are very small.

G KAPKA: In the case of the steel-fibre reinforced matrix there are no problems because the coefficients of thermal expansion of fibre and matrix are virtually the same. The problems are likely to arise where there is a difference. What concerns me somewhat is the degradation of glass-fibre reinforced material over ten years. If I remember correctly, from what I have seen on the screen, the strength falls by a factor of 4 over ten years. Perhaps this is a result of some difference in the coefficient of thermal expansion between the glass fibres and the matrix.

M W FORDYCE (Building Design Partnership, UK): I cannot recall off-the-cuff the coefficient of thermal expansion of glass fibres. The overall coefficient of thermal expansion of GRC as a material is not very different from that of the mortars from which the mix is made. In terms of the mechanisms of strength loss, I do not think that there is any contribution from thermal expansion differences. The strength losses are due to chemical interactions between the fibre and the cement matrix.

As for any possible problems with properties due to thermal expansion differences, in the actual weathering programmes, GRC materials have been exposed to a variety of climates, and the final property of the material has been measured. If there were any effect due to thermal expansion - I do not think that there is - account would have been taken of it in those results.

G KAPKA: All of the stress/strain curves that have been shown today appear to look very much alike, and all of them appear to have been the results of experiments carried out at room temperature. Has anybody measured stress/strain curves of the same material with the same proportion of fibre at, say, $-10^{\circ}C$, $0^{\circ}C$, $20^{\circ}C$ or $40^{\circ}C$? If tests were carried out in such a manner, the effect of differing coefficients of thermal expansion would be apparent. In other words, if the fibre coefficient was larger than that of the cement paste, a higher concentration of fibre at a higher temperature would reduce the initial crack point, and eventually the ultimate strength point.

Let us confine the question to something simpler. Have the same stress/strain experiments been conducted at different temperatures, or have they all been done at room temperature?

H KRENCHEL: I was a little afraid of the first question because we have done very few experiments which point directly at the problem of the differences in thermal expansion coefficients of the plastic material and the cement matrix. I preferred the later question. We have carried out a series of tests at different temperatures on the stress/strain curves of the plate material which we make with polypropylene fibre reinforcements in a neat cement matrix. We had a thermal insulated box in which there was the full set up for the bending test, fully equipped with strain gauges etc., at top and bottom of the test specimen, just as we always have it, and as I showed on Figure 11. We used a small furnace to heat the samples and the tests were carried out at $20^{o}C$, $40^{o}C$, $60^{o}C$, $80^{o}C$, and so on all the way to 140° Celsius. The stress/strain curves were measured when the material had been kept at these temperatures for 24 hours. It was really done thoroughly, and for bending test stress/strain curves there was no change at all in the material to be detected up to about $100^{o}C$. At $110^{o}C$ the strength reduced slightly, as did the E-modulus, and it reduced further at $120^{o}C$, and at $140^{o}C$. At the latter two temperatures the polypropylene has - naturally - lost a good deal of its strength and elastic modulus.

We have not yet carried out similar tests at the lower temperatures and although we have done some work with cooling, I cannot yet refer to it. The other effects of too much expansion from the fibre are negligible. This is one of the points where there is a benefit from the lower E-modulus of plastic fibres than of most other fibres.

Dr P SULLIVAN (Imperial College, London, UK): A question was asked about the thermal coefficient of expansion of cement, concrete and steel fibres. Rather than thermal coefficient of expansion, I would prefer to discuss the overall movement of these various materials with increasing temperature.

Take a cement paste, when it is heated. First it expands, then it contracts, and after that it expands again. When it is cooled down it will contract along a line as shown in Figure A and if re-heated, will follow this same line. If gravel aggregate concrete is heated, the length change goes along quite different lines, which are non-linear. If the temperature is held constant at $200^{\circ}C$, then the material will shrink but if one were to continue increasing the temperature up to $400^{\circ}C$, say, then instead of shrinkage there would be a non-reversible expansion. Further heating and cooling would be represented by lines as shown in Figure B. If a different type of aggregate, say a lightweight aggregate, were to be used, then on first heating the apparent thermal coefficient would be approximately 7 to 10 x 10^{-6} per degree C, but the coefficient would become nearly zero at just over $100^{\circ}C$ before increasing again to a value of about 5 x 10^{-6}. On cooling contraction follows a curve as the temperature increases with a large residual shrinkage at $20^{\circ}C$. On reheating a near linear reversible coefficient of expansion equal to approximately 5 x 10^{-6} per degree C.

The thermal coefficient of expansion of steel is not linear. It will start linear, below $80^{\circ}C$ at a value of 12 to 14 x 10^{-6}, but if one carries on heating, it will start changing and go up to 16 or 18 x 10^{-6} per degree C at a temperature of $400^{\circ}C$.

So, rather than talk about thermal coefficient of expansion, one should really talk about overall movement; that is the effect of the expansion, plus shrinkage, or expansions in certain cases.

The fibres, if they are steel fibres, will follow the changes in the curve. The expansion characteristics of glass are similar to gravel and the expansion coefficient would be in the region of 10 x 10^{-6} per $^{\circ}C$. I would suspect that it would also change with temperature in a similar fashion to gravel concrete.

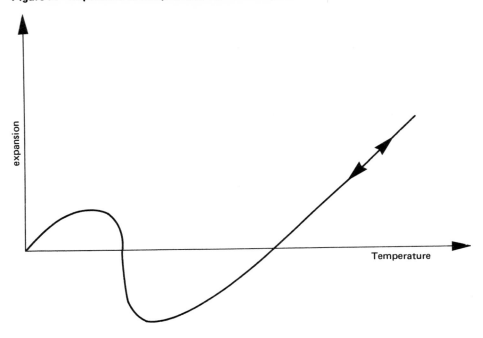

Figure A   Expansion vs temperature for cement paste.

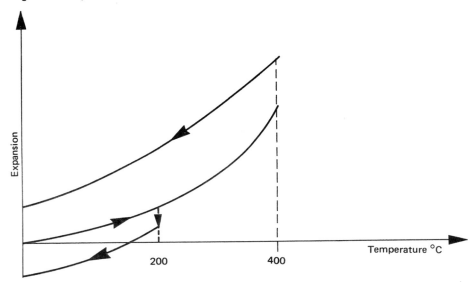

Figure B   Expansion vs temperature for gravel concrete.

SUMMING UP

C W YU - Chairman (Harris & Sutherland, UK):

In this afternoon's session, the various speakers have given us a fairly

comprehensive review on the manufacture, application and design of fibre

reinforced cement/concrete.   The fibres under discussion are steel fibre,

glass fibre and other organic fibre.   For those of us who are interested

in promoting the use of these materials, it is encouraging to note that valuable efforts have been made by the speakers and others to further the understanding of the mechanical properties of these materials, to extend their wide application and to illustrate how, when applied to industry, time and money will be saved.   I am especially interested to study Mr Fordyce's proposed design procedure for GRC members.   We should also be grateful to him for drawing our attention to the subtle difference between FRC and GRC as commonly used.   The former applies to fibre reinforced cement or concrete and the latter applies to glass fibre reinforced cement.   In the former case the fibres can be steel, plastic, glass or asbestos.   In the case of steel fibre concrete, its potential application to industry has been known to engineers for some time.   The high tensile strength, high energy absorption and thermal shock resistant properties of refractory products made from steel fibre concrete have been used to advantage in the steel industry, petrochemical industry, power industry, etc.   Mr Hackman illustrated these clearly.   The many successful applications in this respect in countries like the USA, the Scandinavian countries and Australia, have been described by Mr Hackman, Dr Skarendahl and Mr Marsden in their presentations.

The design approach of GRC members as given by Mr Fordyce is a valuable attempt to find a reasonable design procedure for structural members constructed of materials like GRC.   He based his approach on the philosophy of Limit State Design!   As a result he introduced various partial factors to take into account quality control, environmental effect, scale effect, time effect, etc.   Some of us may feel that the values of most of the partial factors suggested in Mr Fordyce's proposal must be considered speculative; many more statistics must be available before they can be used with confidence.   Perhaps those of us who have the opportunity to use GRC members should co-operate with Mr Fordyce by providing him with additional data on observed performance and strength under the influence of various parameters.   He may thus have further statistical data to enable him to refine his approach.

Mr Smith and Mr Walker described in detail the application of GRC in architectural cladding, walling systems, steel furniture, pipes, sewer lining, water channels, culverts, canal linings, tanks and many other applications in agriculture and in-situ construction. The examples illustrated indicated the rate and breadth of the development of GRC since its early days.

In Part III of this afternoon's discussion, Mr Kosonen of Finland and Mr Guertz of The Netherlands described how the ban or restriction on the use of asbestos cement has led to the development work on replacing asbestos fibre by cellulose fibre and polymer film in the manufacturing of sheet and pipe products. It has been demonstrated that these two fibre cements have comparable mechanical properties to asbestos cement under working conditions. The cost and ease of manufacturing presented no problem either. The development is thus most encouraging, as the health hazard associated with asbestos cement can be avoided in the construction industry. However, the production of these products may be considered as in the pilot stage. Their commercial viability and engineering acceptability have yet to be established.

Errata (in 'CI80 Fibrous Concrete' - D J Hannant)

The formula at the end of line 5, paragraph 4, on page 3 should read $\varepsilon_{fu} - 0.341\alpha \, \varepsilon_{mu}$.

Admixtures

Mechanisms and effects of air-entrainment in concrete

C L Page
University of Aston, Birmingham, UK

Introduction

Air-entrained concrete is concrete containing a dispersion of small air voids, the majority of which are within the size range 20 μm to 1 mm. These voids are uniformly distributed throughout the cement paste as a result of the deliberate inclusion in the mix of an air-entraining agent and they are thus distinguished from the generally much larger, irregular voids of entrapped air that may be present in mixes where compaction is inadequate. Whilst the effects of entrapped air are invariably detrimental to the properties of concrete, the judicious use of air-entrainment allows concretes to be produced with properties, in several respects, superior to those of normal mixes.

The most significant effects of air-entrainment arise in relation to improvement of the durability of hardened concrete exposed to the action of freezing and thawing and to the associated effects induced by de-icing salts. It was, in fact, the accidental discovery, made during the 1930s, that winter deterioration of concrete roads in parts of the U.S.A. was reduced in cases where the cement used incorporated beef tallow (as a grinding aid in manufacture) that led to recognition of the importance of entrained air since it was established that the beef tallow was functioning as an air-entraining agent (1). The finding paved the way for more systematic investigations and, for many years, air-entrainment has been an accepted measure for combatting freezing and thawing damage to exposed concrete. Even in the U.K., where frost causes relatively few problems, it has become normal practice to use air-entrained mixes for pavements and aircraft runways.

Nature of Air-Entraining Agents

A variety of substances have been discovered which are capable of functioning as air-entraining agents for concrete. The major commercial products are formulated from the following classes of material:

a) Natural wood resins and their soaps, e.g. Vinsol resin, which is based on abietic acid,

b) Animal or vegetable fats and oils and their associated fatty acids and soaps, e.g. oleic acid, $CH_3(CH_2)_7CH=CH(CH_2)_7COOH$.

c) Alkali salts of various sulphonated or sulphated organic compounds, e.g. sodium p-dodecylbenzene sulphonate,

In each case, the materials concerned are anionic surfactants. Their polar/non-polar molecular character causes them to be adsorbed at air/water interfaces with the hydrophobic end of the molecule oriented towards the air. The polar end-group, which is present at the water side of the interface, is attractive to the surfaces of cement particles and thus, within a cement paste, a stable dispersion of bubbles is promoted (2, 3). It may be noted, however, that there has been some debate as to whether, in view of the limited solubilities of calcium salts of certain agents, factors besides adsorption from the solution phase may play a significant role with respect to bubble stabilisation in cement paste (4, 5).

The use of air-entraining agents introduces several significant changes to the properties of concrete. In this paper, the prime consideration will be effects on freeze-thaw durability but discussion of this will be preceded by a summary of the influences of air-entrainment on properties generally and their implications with regard to mix design.

General Effects on Concrete Properties

As far as fresh concrete is concerned, the principal effects of air-entrainment are to improve workability and to promote cohesiveness. The former of these characteristics makes it possible to achieve a reduction in the water content required for a given level of workability (6, 7) and the effect may be used as a means of largely offsetting the direct loss of strength which the entrainment of air voids into a mix necessarily implies. The tendency to promote cohesiveness and a reduction in bleeding is generally allowed for by decreasing the proportion of fine aggregate in the concrete (8) and the property is particularly useful in cases where fine aggregates, that are somewhat deficient in the lower particle size ranges, are being used (9).

As regards the effects of air-entrainment on properties of hardened concrete, the influence on strength, for the reasons just stated, is not nearly as drastic as might be inferred from the 'rule-of-thumb' which suggests that each 1% of air voids in a mix is roughly equivalent to a 5.5% loss in strength (6). In practice, air-entrained mixes comparable in strength and workability to plain concretes can usually be designed without the need for substantial increases in cement content (9).

The resistances of air-entrained concretes to elastic deformation (10), creep (11) and shrinkage (12) appear to be generally comparable with those of plain concrete of similar strength. Other aspects of the long term performance of concrete, such as impermeability to various aggressive substances and resistance to sulphate attack, have been found to be somewhat improved by moderate amounts of air-entrainment (6).

Frost Action on Hardened Concrete

Before proceeding to consider the influence of entrained air in reducing the susceptibility of concrete to frost damage and de-icing salt action, it is necessary to examine briefly the nature of freezing and thawing effects that occur in concrete and similar porous materials. The subject is somewhat involved because, in practice, frost action will comprise a wide range of macroscopic and microscopic phenomena involving concretes of varying degrees of saturation being frozen at different rates and frequencies.

The frost resistance of hardened concrete depends on characteristics of both aggregate and cement paste and clearly it is the effect of the latter which is important in relation to the functions of air-entraining agents. The water that is present within pores of different sizes in hardened cement paste requires different levels of cooling below the bulk freezing temperature in order to support its transformation into thermodynamically stable crystals of ice. This gives rise to the concept that, during a cycle of freezing, ice formation begins in the largest cavities and gradually spreads to smaller pores as the temperature is progressively reduced. A substantial fraction of the water in the system, however, remains effectively unfreezable over the complete range of temperatures likely to be experienced.

The important consequence of freezing within a pore that was originally filled with aqueous solution is the generation of dilatant pressure within the remaining liquid. This reacts against the pore walls and, in the absence of relieving mechanisms, irreversible expansion of the material may occur. The mechanism of this effect in hardened cement paste has been extensively researched and several theories have been proposed which lay emphasis on a number of possible causes of pressure generation. These have included, inter alia, hindered hydraulic flow in response to the volume expansion associated with ice formation (13, 14), preferential growth of large ice crystals owing to surface energy considerations (15), osmotic pressures due to the solute-enriched layer of solution formed in the vicinity of growing ice crystals (16), and restricted desorption of unfreezable water from the surfaces of gel particles owing to temperature-dependent change in the chemical potential of the adsorbate (17, 18).

The presence of de-icing salts introduces additional complications, exacerbating the effects of normal freezing and thawing by mechanisms which are not yet fully resolved. Their action appears to depend primarily on physical, rather than specific chemical, interaction and intermediate salt concentrations give rise to maximal rates of deterioration (19). Several theories concerning their role have been advanced and these have been reviewed recently (20).

Despite the uncertainties that exist concerning mechanisms of expansion caused by frost and de-icing salt action, it is possible to explain the beneficial influence of air-entrainment simply, albeit incompletely, in terms of the stress-relieving characteristics of the dispersion of air voids in the hardened cement paste. The available free spaces thus provided are capable of accommodating movements of water and ice without generation of the large internal pressure gradients normally associated with such processes. In view of the fact that freezing of air-entrained cement pastes results in transference of water from full pores to originally empty voids, the effect may be characterised by a shrinkage of the material, in contrast to the expansion accompanying the freezing of plain cement pastes (16).

In order for the protection conferred by entrained air to be effective, however, it is necessary that the thickness of cement paste between adjacent air voids should be everywhere less than a critical value beyond which the pressure-relieving mechanism ceases to be exerted. The magnitude of this critical thickness has been estimated from theoretical considerations on the basis of the 'hydraulic pressure' mechanism (21, 14) and practical experience indicates that mean bubble spacings generally have to be maintained below a maximum of about 400 μm for there to be any significant improvement in frost resistance (22). It is found to be desirable from the point of view of achieving maximum durability that they should be restricted to perhaps 20% of this limiting value.

Characteristics of Air Void Systems in Air-Entrained Concrete

In view of the importance of bubble spacing in relation to the performance of air-entrained concrete, there has been a considerable amount of research aimed at characterisation of the void system and determination of factors that influence it. For hardened concrete, it is possible to determine by means of linear traverse microscopy parameters such as the specific surface area of the air voids and the bubble 'spacing factor', which provides a useful index of the maximum distance of any point in the cement paste from the periphery of a nearby air void (23). The time required for performing these laborious measurements may be substantially reduced as a result of recent developments in the use of image-analysing microscopes (24). Unfortunately, however, such information cannot be obtained for plastic mixes and, for purposes of routine quality control, air-entrained concrete is assessed generally on the basis of the more readily determined total air content of the material. It is usual for this to be maintained within the range 3 - 6% when producing frost-resistant concretes of varying mix proportions.

There are many factors that influence the quantity of air and the bubble size distribution present in samples of air-entrained concrete.

Clearly the nature of the air-entraining agent used and its dosage are of paramount importance. It appears that increasing dosages of a given agent will result in increasing volumes of entrained air, but that the effect diminishes at high concentrations so that a maximum air content is eventually reached which depends on the type of agent and mix characteristics (25). The mean specific surface area of the entrained bubbles is dependent on the nature of the agent used (26) and, although not fully understood, the differences may be ascribable to variations in the extent to which different agents cause lowering of surface tension, increase in mechanical stability of air bubbles and changes in the viscosity of the paste (4).

Other mix variables also have pronounced effects on the quantity and distribution of entrained air. In particular, the amount of air entrained by a given dosage of agent tends to decrease with increasing cement content (7), whilst the specific surface area of the voids at constant air content increases with the proportion of cement; characteristics of the cement such as fineness (27) and alkali content (28) also have a considerable bearing on the dosage of a given agent required to entrain a prescribed volume of air. As regards the effects of aggregates, there appears to be no direct influence exerted by the coarse aggregate on the quantity of entrained air (9). The volume of cement paste per

148

unit volume of concrete, however, is obviously related to the maximum size of
the aggregate used and thus recommended air contents, expressed as percentages
of the volume of concrete, are dependent on the maximum size of the coarse
aggregate - see, for example (25). The proportion and grading of fine aggregate
in a mix do have a direct effect on the capacity to entrain air. In general,
increases in fine aggregate content lead to increasing quantities of voids being
produced by a given dosage of a particular agent and it appears that the
proportion of particles within the size range 300 - 600 μm is of most
significance because their packing arrangement within the mortar largely
determines the total volume of spaces of appropriate sizes (< 100 μm) to
accommodate the majority of entrained air bubbles (29); the surface texture of
the fine aggregate is also somewhat influential in this respect (30). In
situations where air-entraining agents are used in conjunction with other
additives, the possibility of modified dosages being required to achieve a given
air content has generally to be taken into consideration.

Besides the effects arising from variations in mix composition, alterations in
physical variables such as temperature (31) and duration of mixing (32) can give
rise to changes in quantities of entrained air, the magnitude of the effects
being dependent on mixing technique, volume and workability of the mixer
charge, etc. After mixing of air-entrained concrete has been completed, it is
necessary that handling and placing operations be properly controlled as failure
to do so can result in reduction in the air content of the material. Vibration
times, in particular, should be kept as short as possible because substantial
losses of air are otherwise liable to occur at this stage (9); since the effect
of vibration, however, is to eliminate most rapidly the largest voids from the
mix, minor reductions in air content arising from this cause are practically
unimportant in terms of their influence on freeze/thaw durability (30, 33).

A further effect, which has been viewed as a potential source of instability of
the bubble system produced by mixing, arises from the thermodynamic tendency
for growth of the larger voids within a random dispersion to be fed by diffusion

of air from smaller neighbouring bubbles (34). The driving force for this is provided by reduction in the total surface energy of the system that would accompany bubble coarsening. It seems doubtful, however, whether the rate of this process in concrete mixes of the normal compositional range is sufficient for it to cause significant changes in void distribution during the interval between mixing and setting (35, 4).

In view of the foregoing discussion, it is clear that the production of air-entrained concrete, in which the air content and bubble spacing are maintained within acceptable limits of variation, depends on the adequacy of quality control procedures followed throughout the various stages of manufacture. Provided suitable measures are taken in this respect, it is nevertheless possible to ensure that the reproducibility of air-entrained mixes will be satisfactory under a wide range of conditions of application, including circumstances which involve the use of special techniques such as pumping and slipforming (9).

An interesting alternative approach to the problem of limiting variability in the void characteristics associated with air-entrained concrete has been provided recently by the suggestion that certain porous particulate admixtures might be used in place of conventional air-entraining agents for improving the freeze/thaw durability of concrete (36). Results obtained from laboratory investigations have indicated that, for example, certain forms of crushed brick particle may be effective in this way. Less promising effects were, however, obtained when various other forms of porous particle were used and it would appear that the performance of such materials is likely to be critically dependent on control of their pore size distributions.

Effects on Durability of Immature Concrete

A final aspect of the effects of air-entrainment that warrants brief consideration is the influence on durability of immature mixes that are exposed to the action of freezing and thawing. It is well known that the exposure of plain concrete or cement paste to frost action at an early stage of curing can result in significant internal damage, which permanently reduces the level of strength attained by the material when long-term normal curing is resumed (37).

The question as to whether air-entrainment might be beneficial from the point of view of reducing this sort of damage has not been subjected to detailed examination. Recently, however, some interesting and unexpected findings have emerged from investigations carried out on a limited scale independently in Britain (38) and the U.S.A. (39). On the basis of results obtained in these studies, it would appear that application of moderate numbers of freezing and thawing cycles to air-entrained cement paste or concrete specimens at early ages may cause the strength developed by the material during subsequent prolonged normal curing to exceed that of specimens cured for similar periods without being frozen.

The explanation of this anomalous effect is by no means clear but its origins must presumably reside in some form of microstructural redistribution of hydration products within the cement paste. Observations that may have some relevance in this context have been made by means of scanning electron microscopy, applied to the fracture surfaces of air-entrained specimens of cement paste which had been exposed to cyclic freezing and thawing at an early stage of curing (40, 41). This revealed the presence within the air-voids of small, equiaxed particles of calcium-rich material which were thought to be composed of portlandite. Their formation could have been the result of precipitation from the solute-enriched solution associated with ice crystals growing inside the air-voids, and their distinctive morphology may have been attributable to the presence of hydrophobic surface layers derived from the air-entraining agent (a wood resin derivative).

It was suggested that this process of rejection of calcium ions from the pore solution during freezing cycles may have been instrumental in limiting growth within the matrix of large, readily-cleaved crystals of portlandite. Since the latter are regarded as strength-reducing features of mature cement pastes (42), it is thus possible to account for the observed enhancement in mechanical properties of air-entrained specimens resulting from early exposure to freezing and thawing.

Further work is required to test this tentative hypothesis and to establish in more detail the response to frost action of immature air-entrained mixes covering a wide range of compositions.

References

1. F.H. Jackson, Proc. Am. Concr. Inst., 40, 509 (1944).

2. G.M. Bruere, Proc. Am. Concr. Inst., 51, 905 (1955).

3. P.C. Kreijger, Proc. Int. Symp. on Admixtures for Mortar and Concrete, Brussels (1967) pp. 33 - 37.

4. T.C. Powers, 'The Properties of Fresh Concrete', Wiley, New York (1968) Chapters 7 & 8.

5. G.M. Bruere, J. Appl. Chem. & Biotechnol., 21, 61 (1971).

6. P.J.F. Wright, Proc. Inst. C.E., Part I, 2(3), 337 (1953).

7. D.F. Cornelius, Road Research Laboratory Report, LR 363 (1970).

8. W.A. Cordon, Proc. Am. Concr. Inst., 42, 605 (1946).

9. M.R. Rixom, 'Chemical Admixtures for Concrete', Spon, London (1978) Chapters 2 & 5.

10. B.W. Shacklock and P.W. Keene, Civ. Eng. & Pub. Works Rev., 54, 77 (1959).

11. M.A. Ward, A.M. Neville and S.P. Singh, Mag. Concr. Res., 21(69), 205 (1969).

12. P.W. Keene, Cement & Concrete Assoc. Tech. Report TRA/331, London (1960).

13. T.C. Powers, Proc. Am. Concr. Inst., 41, 245 (1945).

14. G. Fagerlund, American Concrete Inst. Publication SP47 (1975) pp. 13 - 66.

15. D.H. Everett, Trans. Faraday Soc., 57, 1541 (1961).

16. T.C. Powers, American Concrete Inst. Publication SP47 (1975) pp. 1 - 12.

17. G.G. Litvan, J. Am. Ceram. Soc., 55, 38 (1972).

18. M.D. Setzer, Proc. Conf. on Hydraulic Cement Pastes: Their Structure and Properties, Sheffield, Cement & Concrete Assoc. (1976) pp. 312 - 325.

19. G.J. Verbeck and P. Klieger, Highway Res. Board Bull., No. 150, pp. 1 - 13, Washington D.C. (1957).

20. V.S. Ramachandran, 'Calcium Chloride in Concrete: Science and Technology', Applied Science Publishers, London (1976) p. 178 ff.

21. T.C. Powers, Proc. Highway Res. Board, 29, 184 (1949).

22. U.S. Bureau of Reclamation, Concrete Laboratory Report No. C-824, Denver, Colorado (April 1956).

23. A.S.T.M. Standard C457 - 71.

24. S. Chatterji and H. Gudmundsson, Cem. Concr. Res., 7, 423 (1977).

25. A.M. Neville, Properties of Concrete, 2nd. ed., Pitman, London (1973) pp. 420 - 421.

26. G.M. Bruere, Australian J. Appl. Sci., 12, 78 (1961).

27. E.W. Scripture, S.W. Benedict and F.J. Litwinowicz, Proc. Am. Concr. Inst., 48, 205 (1952).

28. W.R. Greening, J.P.C.A. Research and Development Laboratories, 9(2), 22 (1967).

29. M.A. Craven, Proc. Am. Concr. Inst., 45, 205 (1949).

30. J.E. Backstrom, R.W. Burrows, R.C. Mielenz and V.E. Wolkodoff, Proc. Am. Concr. Inst., 55, 359 (1958/9).

31. S. Walker and D.L. Bloem, Proc. Am. Concr. Inst., 42, 629 (1946).

32. E.W. Scripture and F.J. Litwinowicz, Proc. Am. Concr. Inst., 45, 653 (1949).

33. H.E. Vivian, Proc. 4th. Int. Symp. on the Chemistry of Cement, Washington D.C. (1960) p. 915.

34. R.C. Mielenz, V.E. Wolkodoff, J.E. Backstrom and H.L. Flack, Proc. Am. Concr. Inst., 55, 95 (1958/9).

35. G.M. Bruere, Australian J. Appl. Sci., 13, 222 (1962).

36. G.G. Litvan and P.J. Sereda, Cem. Concr. Res., 8, 53 (1978).

37. O.A. Kayyali, C.L. Page and A.G.B. Ritchie, Proc. Conf. on Hydraulic Cement Pastes: Their Structure and Properties, Sheffield, Cement & Concrete Assoc. (1976) pp. 204 - 219.

38. O.A. Kayyali, C.L. Page and A.G.B. Ritchie, Proc. Am. Concr. Inst., 76, 1217 (1979).

39. B.D. Barnes, R.L. Ordorff and J.E. Roten, Proc. Am. Concr. Inst., 74, 612 (1977).

40. O.A. Kayyali, Ph.D. Thesis, University of Strathclyde (1976).

41. O.A. Kayyali, C.L. Page and A.G.B. Ritchie, Proc. Am. Concr. Inst. (in press).

42. R.B. Williamson, Progress in Materials Science, 15(3), 189 - 285 (1972).

Specifications and standards for concrete admixtures – an international review

T J Tipler
Cement and Concrete Association, UK

SUMMARY

This paper reviews a number of Standard specifications and approval regulations for concrete admixtures. Information is presented on the specifications given in the relevant documents from 12 countries. Their requirements relating to uniformity and performance are compared in detail for five simple types of admixture having one main action. Some of the uncertainties involved in specifying performance requirements are briefly discussed.

INTRODUCTION

Background

In 1950 the American Society for Testing and Materials published a tentative Standard specification for air-entraining admixtures for concrete [1]. Twelve years later the first edition of their Standard specification for chemical admixtures appeared [2]. Standard specifications for calcium chloride for use in concrete were published in Spain [3] in 1958 and in the United Kingdom [4] in 1963 but these did not include performance requirements. It was not until the last decade that the majority of existing Standard specifications came into being. At present at least 12 countries possess such Standards [1 - 19] and in several other countries regulations [20 - 24] governing the approval of admixtures exist. Also in the 1970's, Codes or Guides on the use of admixtures were published in Australia [25], Canada [26], Denmark [27] and the United States [28] and in 1975 the RILEM Working Group produced their Final Report on the use, classification, quality control and testing of admixtures [29].

Objectives of specifications

Mr Mather has pointed out in the preceding paper that a specification for a concrete admixture should serve several purposes. For each type of admixture to which it relates, a comprehensive specification should have the aim of ensuring that a particular admixture will

1. be acceptably uniform from consignment to consignment
2. modify the properties of concrete in the manner required

3. have no significantly deleterious effects in the short or long term on concrete, its reinforcement or items embedded in it

4. suffer no misuse or deterioration due to unsatisfactory marking, delivery or storage

5. be used correctly and safely

Requirements of specifications

The scope of Standard specifications for admixtures and of other Regulations governing their approval varies considerably from country to country both in respect of the types of admixture covered and the substance of their requirements. The Romanian Standards [15,16], for example, only deal with two specific types of water-reducing admixture and contain no performance requirements. The more comprehensive documents are concerned with a broader spectrum of admixture types and contain, inter alia, sections dealing with

1. Uniformity requirements

2. Performance requirements

3. Presence of halogenides and reducing sugars

4. Information to be provided by the manufacturer or vendor

5. Marking

Their aim therefore reflects that outlined above.

In this paper the Standard specifications from ten countries and the Regulations governing approval of admixtures in two others are compared. For five simple types of admixture having one main action, the uniformity and performance requirements of the Standards and Regulations reviewed are presented in some detail. Several of the documents contain details of the methods to be used for testing admixtures but a discussion of these tests is not attempted here.

STANDARDS AND REGULATIONS REVIEWED AND TYPES OF ADMIXTURE COVERED

Standard specifications

Australia [5], Austria [6], Belgium [7], Bulgaria [8], Canada [9,10], Columbia [11], France [12], Israel [13], Italy [14], Romania [15,16], the United Kingdom [17,18,19] and the United States [1,2] have all published Standard specifications for admixtures. An immediate difficulty arises in comparing Standards because of differences in terminology and definition. In the absence of an ISO Standard on classification, the definitions of admixtures given in the RILEM Working Group Final Report [29] have been adopted wherever possible. The admixture types to which the above Standards relate are listed in three groups in Table 1. The first group contains simple types of admixture having one main action. The second group contains those admixtures which combine two of the main actions from the first group. The third group contains admixtures whose definitions do not have a counterpart in the RILEM classification. The description of an admixture given in a Standard will not necessarily correspond to the RILEM description given in this paper. The Austrian Standard [6], for example, purports to deal with "Antifreezing" admixtures but under the RILEM classification it actually relates to "Accelerators of hardening", "Water-reducing accelerators of hardening" and "Air-entraining accelerators of hardening".

The types of admixture covered by the Standards of the individual countries listed above are shown in Table 2.

Regulations governing approval of admixtures

The French Standard NF P18 - 103 [12] deals primarily with classification, definitions and marking. The Regulations governing the approval of admixtures in France [20] are issued by COPLA (Commission Permanente des Liants Hydrauliques et des Adjuvants du Beton). These Regulations contain very comprehensive uniformity and performance requirements.

In Germany the Code for the design and construction of concrete and reinforced concrete structures [30] only permits the use of admixtures having a valid test mark. The Directives governing the allocation of test marks [21] and the control [22] and testing [23] of admixtures are issued by the Institut für Bautechnik in Berlin. These Directives relate to water-reducing, air-entraining, set-retarding, accelerating and permeability-reducing admixtures. The Institute does not carry out testing of admixtures but administers the approval system and issues test marks.

The requirements of COPLA and the Institut für Bautechnik have been included in this review for comparison with the national Standard specifications listed above except for that of Columbia [11]. The latter has not been included in the detailed comparison of specification requirements which follows because of its close similarity to ASTM C494 [2].

PRESCRIPTIVE AND UNIFORMITY REQUIREMENTS OF SPECIFICATIONS

In the majority of specifications these relate to the admixture itself. The RILEM Working Group Final Report [29] lists 20 tests suitable for the adequate categorisation of an admixture. These tests are:

General

1. Physical state

Content of particular constituents

2. Dry solid content
3. Loss on ignition

4. Insoluble residue after ignition

5. Presence of sugars

6. Chloride content

7. Sulphate content

8. Nitrate and ammonia contents

9. Phosphate content

Special properties

10. pH

11. Surface tension

12. Foam stability

13. Specific surface

14. Specific mass }
15. Specific volume }

16. Freezing

17. Electro chemical behaviour

Identification

18. Infra red and/or X - ray spectra }
19. X - ray fluorescence }

20. Check on validity of manufacturer's methods of indentification

Clearly not all these tests are appropriate for all admixtures; test 12, for example, is only relevant to air-entraining admixtures and test 13 to powdered admixtures. Most of the documents reviewed call for markedly fewer tests than those listed above. The RILEM Final Report does in fact suggest that only tests 1 and 2, 18 (or 19) and 20 are needed for the quality control of an admixture.

Table 3 indicates those attributes of admixtures upon which compliance limits are placed by the Standards and Regulations discussed. Particular documents specify different combinations of these requirements for different admixtures depending upon their type. The compliance criteria are given in the form of allowable tolerances on

a) the values obtained for the initial sample [2]

   or

b) the mean values declared by the manufacturer, [13,18]

or in the form of the manufacturer's declared deviations [17] from (b) above.

PERFORMANCE REQUIREMENTS OF SPECIFICATIONS

General

These requirements are concerned with the relative performance of paste, mortar and/or concrete containing the admixture (test mixes) compared to that of the corresponding paste, mortar or concrete, usually of similar consistence, containing the same materials but no admixture (reference mixes). Whether performance requirements are laid down for the behaviour of paste, mortar and concrete, of one or other of these, or of combinations of two of them, varies from specification to specification. Table 4 shows for the individual Standards and Regulations reviewed the types of test and reference mixes for which compliance limits are imposed.

Test and reference mixes

Reference pastes and mortars are usually the standard ones used in cement testing in the country concerned [6,7,14,20]. Test mixes are similar mixes containing the admixture, the water content being adjusted to give the same consistence. For concrete, each specification details the reference mix with particular regard to cement content and consistence. The stipulated mean cement content ranges from 270 kg/m^3 [6,10] to 350 kg/m^3 [20] and the mean slumps specified vary from 50 mm [8] to 100 mm [13]. In the relevant UK Standard [18] consistence is quoted in terms of compacting factor and the mean value specified is 0.87. In Austria [6] and Belgium [7] the required consistence is specified in terms of flow table values.

Considerable importance is attached to the constituent materials for the test and reference mixes but the approach to their choice is far from uniform. The most onerous requirements are those contained in the COPLA Technical Regulations [20] which call for both low C_3A and high C_3A cements from named works to be used in separate test and reference mixes for all performance requirements. These regulations also stipulate the source and overall grading of the aggregate to be used. In contrast ASTM C494 [2] recommends that, except where tests relate to specific uses, a thorough blend of equal parts of three cements from three mills should be used. It specifies the grading of coarse and fine aggregate but otherwise just requires them to come from single lots which conform to the ASTM specification for concrete aggregates. British Standard BS 5075: Part 1 [18] specifies in particular the use of a selected "typical" ordinary Portland cement.

Performance requirements in cement paste

These are imposed by the Austrian [6], Belgian [7], Bulgarian [8] and Italian [14] standards and by the German Institut für Bautechnik directives [21 to 23]. They relate to such characteristics as water for standard consistence, initial and final setting times and volume stability or soundness. For five simple types of admixture these compliance criteria are given in Table 5.

(NOTE In Table 5 and in the later Tables 6 and 7, R represents the value of the characteristic concerned obtained on the reference paste, mortar or concrete mix.)

Performance requirements in mortar

These are imposed for certain types of admixture by the Austrian [6], Belgian [7], Italian [14] and United States [1] standards and by the French COPLA regulations. They relate to differing selections of the following characteristics

1. Water reduction
2. Consistence (at same w/c ratio)
3. Air content
4. Bleeding
5. Setting times
6. Heat of hydration
7. Strength, compressive and flexural
8. Shrinkage
9. Capillary absorption

For five simple types of admixture the compliance criteria specified are indicated in Table 6.

Performance requirements in concrete

Most Standard specifications now require admixtures to meet performance requirements in concrete. They are imposed on differing selections of the following characteristics

1. Water reduction or water content
2. Consistence (at same w/c ratio)
3. Air content
4. Bleeding
5. Setting or stiffening time
6. Compressive strength
7. Tensile strength
8. Shrinkage
9. Freeze-thaw resistance

For water-reducing, air-entraining and set-retarding admixtures and for accelerators of hardening and permeability-reducing admixtures the relevant compliance criteria from the documents reviewed are indicated in Tables 7.1 to 7.5 respectively. When comparing these compliance criteria **for** any given property, one must remember that individual countries may have employed different test methods and conditions of testing when measuring it.

INFORMATION TO BE PROVIDED BY THE MANUFACTURER OR VENDOR

Among the Standards reviewed, those of Austria [7], Canada [10], Israel [13] and the United Kingdom [18] specify in most detail the information which the manufacturer/vendor must, or can be required to, supply. This information is, of course, designed to ensure that an admixture is identified properly, is handled and stored adequately and is used correctly and safely. Taken together, the above standards either require, or allow the purchaser to require, the manufacturer/vendor to furnish the following types of information

1. Identification of admixture by name, type, etc.

2. Details of acceptance and uniformity tests

3. Details of any certification, ie. of conformance to standard

4. Recommended normal and maximum dosage

5. Effects of underdosage and overdosage

6. Secondary effects on air content, setting/stiffening, or colour, of concrete

7. Instructions for transport and storage

8. Instructions for use including any restrictions on use and any necessary safety precautions

9. Physical state

10. Composition including type of main active ingredient

11. Chloride content

12. Sugar content

13. Any known incompatibility with other materials

MARKING

A number of the Standards (2,6,10,12,13,16,18) contain stipulations about marking. These largely reflect the need to convey on packaging or a delivery label, appropriate items of information from the above list. Some standards also require several of the following items to be marked

a) quantity

b) identity of production lot

c) any limit on storage life

d) endorsement of conformity to the Standard, or, of approval and

e) number of the relevant Standard.

DISCUSSION

Prescriptive or uniformity requirements

To give assurance that an admixture is uniform within a consignment, or equivalent from consignment to consignment, or to an acceptance sample, specifications require the measured values of certain attributes to lie within specified limits. It can be seen from Table 3 that the choice of these attributes varies considerably from country to country, the Belgian requirements being the most onerous. The most frequently specified attributes are:

1. Dry solids content

2. Chloride content

3. pH

4. Relative density

No individual country's selection corresponds exactly to the combination of checks recommended by the RILEM Final Report [29] and given earlier in this paper. That of Australia [5] approaches it. Only two countries' Standards, those of Australia [5] and the United States [2] make provision for the similarity of the infra red absorption spectra of initial and test samples to be checked. These tests are, however, optional.

Performance requirements

The compliance criteria laid down by different countries for five simple types of admixture have been indicated in Tables 5, 6 and 7. The characteristics or properties upon which limits are placed as well as the test methods employed to measure them vary widely from country to country. In individual specifications, however, the performance requirements selected are designed to give assurance that each type of admixture will perform in the required manner and will not adversely affect the concrete properties by, for example, increasing bleeding, final setting time or shrinkage, or by reducing strength or durability.

The problems inherent in testing admixture performance arise from two main sources.

1. Differences between the constituent materials used to make the concrete which is tested and those used for a specific job.

2. Differences between test conditions and job conditions.

In the first instance, the interactions between an admixture and differing constituent materials will vary, thus affecting its performance. The interaction between an admixture and an ordinary Portland cement will be affected mainly by the C_3A content and alkali content of the cement. In certain other cements the proportion of clinker to slag or pozzolana will be important [29]. The RILEM Final Report suggests that, depending upon the country concerned, tests should be made using several cements. Only the French COPLA Regulations [20] require the use of more than one cement; they specify that two named cements, one of relatively low C_3A content and one of relatively high C_3A content, shall be used. An admixture which performs satisfactorily with a "typical" cement or one blended from, say, three mills will not necessarily give similar performance when used with a different cement. The presence of pozzolans in a mix can affect the performance of an admixture; it is well known that pulverized fuel ash can reduce the effectiveness of an air-entraining admixture. Similarly admixture performance can be affected in various ways by aggregates having different properties and grading and by hardness or softness of mixing water. ASTM C494 [2] recommends that for testing for specific uses, those materials to be incorporated in the concrete for the job should be employed.

In the second instance, test conditions are chosen to give standardized testing in the laboratory [2]. Admixture performance on site, however, may be adversely affected by differences in such items as ambient or concrete temperature, workability, time of agitation, type and degree of compaction, actual freeze-thaw conditions occurring etc.

Chloride content

As indicated in Table 3 several countries place compliance limits on the chloride content of admixtures. There is also an increasing tendency effectively to ban or severely restrict the use of chloride-based accelerators in prestressed and reinforced concrete and in concrete containing embedded metals [6,30,31].

Sampling and testing variability

The producer and consumer risks involved in applying the compliance criteria given in the specifications reviewed are affected by the magnitude of the testing variability. Some allowance for testing variability is explicitly made in the Canadian Standards [9,10] and in the COPLA Regulations [20]. The 1979 edition of ASTM C494 [2] contains precision statements for two types of uniformity test. Elsewhere some allowance for testing variability is thought to be implicit in the rather low level of relative performance required of test mixes. As an example of this, the 5% water reduction generally required of test mixes containing water-reducing admixtures may be quoted.

Cost

The cost of testing involved in specifying comprehensive performance requirements [20] should be balanced against the benefit of increased assurance. In making such an assessment, the high cost of building failures must be borne in mind.

CONCLUSIONS

The documents reviewed contain much detailed and useful information on the methods currently employed to specify admixtures. The considerable activity in standardization in this field in the past decade marks the increasing use of admixtures throughout the world, the growing expertise of manufacturers and the accompanying need of users for confidence in the performance and reliability of admixtures. The existence of these

Standards and Regulations should contribute to the wider acceptance of admixtures as useful and for some purposes essential constituents of concrete.

Compliance of an admixture with the requirements of the more comprehensive type of specification will increase confidence in its use but the empirical nature of existing performance tests and the complexities of the interactions between the materials in concrete prevent such compliance being a sure guarantee of performance in every concrete. Limited trial mixes and tests to check certain aspects of performance for specific uses will continue to be desirable. Perhaps in the future specifications will be able to invoke the use of more fundamental tests of admixtures and so give users even greater confidence in complying materials.

ACKNOWLEDGEMENTS

The Author wishes to thank the Library staff at the British Standards Institution and the Cement and Concrete Association for their patient help.

REFERENCES

1. AMERICAN SOCIETY FOR TESTING AND MATERIALS. ANSI/ASTM C 260-77. Standard specification for air-entraining admixtures for concrete. 1979 Annual book of ASTM Standards. Part 14. Philadelphia. pp. 182-185.

2. AMERICAN SOCIETY FOR TESTING AND MATERIALS. ANSI/ASTM C 494-79. Standard specification for chemical admixtures for concrete. 1979 Annual book of ASTM Standards. Part 14. Philadelphia. pp. 302-312.

3. INSTITUTO NACIONAL DE RACIONALIZACIÓN DEL TRABAJO. UNE 41 113:1958. Cloruro cálcico, utilizado como producto de adición en los hormigones. (Calcium chloride for use as a concrete admixture). Madrid. pp. 1.

4. BRITISH STANDARDS INSTITUTION. BS 3587:1963. Specifications for calcium chloride. (Technical.) London. pp. 9. (With Amendment No. 1. April, 1972.)

5. STANDARDS ASSOCIATION OF AUSTRALIA. AS 1478:1973. Chemical admixtures for use in concrete. Sydney. pp. 20. (With Amendment No. 1. May 1974 and Amendment No. 2. July 1978.)

6. ÖSTERREICHISCHES NORMUNGSINSTITUT. ÖNORM B 3332:1971. Zusatzmittel für Mörtel und Beton. Frostschutzmittel. (Admixtures for mortar and concrete. Antifreezing agents.) Vienna. pp. 7.

7. INSTITUT BELGE DE NORMALISATION. NBN T61-101:1979. Adjuvants pour mortiers et bétons. Spécifications pour les réducteurs d'eau, entraîneurs d'air, réducteurs d'eau-entraîneurs d'air, réducteurs de perméabilité, retardateurs de prise, accélérateurs de prise et accélérateurs de durcissement. (Admixtures for mortar and concrete. Specifications for

water - reducers, air - entrainers, permeability - reducers, set - retarders, set - accelerators and accelerators of hardening.) Brussels. pp. 7.

8. BULGARIAN STATE STANDARDISATION COMMITTEE. BSS 14069 - 77. Concrete admixtures. Classification and technical requirements. pp. 4. (In Bulgarian.)

9. CANADIAN STANDARDS ASSOCIATION. CAN 3 - A 266.1 - M 78. Air-entraining admixtures for concrete. Rexdale. pp. 19.

10. CANADIAN STANDARDS ASSOCIATION. CAN 3 - A266.2 - M 78. Chemical admixtures for concrete. Rexdale. pp. 23.

11. INSTITUTO COLUMBIANO DE NORMAS TECNICAS. INCONTEC 1299:1978. Aditivos químocos para hormigón. (Chemical admixtures for concrete.) Bogota. pp. 9.

12. ASSOCIATION FRANÇAISE DE NORMALISATION. NF P18 - 103: 72. Définitions et marquage des adjuvants du béton. (Definitions and marking of concrete admixtures.) Paris. pp.5.

13. STANDARDS INSTITUTION OF ISRAEL. SI 896:1976. Chemical admixtures for concrete. (Translation without guarantee.) Tel Aviv. pp. 11.

14. ENTE NAZIONALE ITALIANO DI UNIFICAZIONE. UNI 7101 to 7109-72. Additivi per impasti cementizi. (Admixtures for cement mixes.) Milan.

15. INSTITUTUL ROMAN DE STANDARDIZARE. STAS 8625-70. Aditiv plastifiant mixt pentru betoane. (Mixed plasticizing admixture for concrete.) Bucharest. pp. 7.

16. INSTITUTUL ROMAN DE STANDARDIZARE. STAS 8626-70. Lignosulfonat de Calciu tehnic. (Calcium lignosulphonate, Technical grade.) Bucharest. pp. 6.

17. BRITISH STANDARDS INSTITUTION. BS 1014:1975. Specification for pigments for Portland cement and Portland cement products. London. pp.11.

18. BRITISH STANDARDS INSTITUTION. BS 5075: Part 1 :1974. Specification for concrete admixtures. Part 1. Accelerating admixtures, retarding admixtures and water - reducing admixtures. London. pp. 17.

19. BRITISH STANDARDS INSTITUTION. Draft standard specification for admixtures. BS 5075 : Part 2: Air - entraining admixtures. Draft for public comment, 1979. pp. 19.

20. COMMISSION PERMANENTE DES LIANTS HYDRAULIQUES ET DES ADJUVANTS DU BÉTON. Règlement technique de l'agrément des adjuvants et des ajouts des bétons. (Technical regulations for the approval of concrete admixtures and supplemen materials.) Ministère de L'Equipement, Paris, 1978.

21. INSTITUT FÜR BAUTECHNIK. Richtlinien für die Zuteilung von Prüfzeichen für Betonzusatzmittel. Fassung März 1973. (Directives for the allocation of test marks for concrete admixtures. March 1973 version.) **Mitteilungen, Heft 3,** 1973. pp. 86 - 88. Wilhelm Ernst und Sohn, Berlin.

22. INSTITUT FÜR BAUTECHNIK. Richtlinien für die Überwachung von Betonzusatz-mitteln. Fassung März 1973. (Directives for the control of concrete admixtures. March 1973 version.) Mitteilungen, Heft 3, 1973. pp. 88 - 90. Wilhelm Ernst und Sohn, Berlin.

23. INSTITUT FÜR BAUTECHNIK. Richtlinien für die Prüfung der Wirksamkeit von Betonzusatzmitteln. Fassung Oktober, 1974. (Directives for testing the efficiency of concrete admixtures. October 1974 version.) Mitteilungen, Heft 1, 1975. pp. 19 - 22. Wilhelm Ernst und Sohn, Berlin.

24. SUOMEN RAKENNUSINSINÖÖRIEN LIITTO FINLANDS BYGGNADSINGENJÖRERS FÖRBUND. Betonin lisäaineiden käyttö. (Use of concrete admixtures.) Helsinki, Suomen Betoniyhdistys r.y., 1969. pp. 41.

25. STANDARDS ASSOCIATION OF AUSTRALIA. AS 1479 : 1973. Code of practice for the use of chemical admixtures in concrete. Sydney. pp. 21 - 35.

26. CANADIAN STANDARDS ASSOCIATION. CAN 3 : A 266.4 : M 78. Guidelines for the use of admixtures in concrete. Rexdale. pp. 43.

27. DANSK INGENIØRFORENINGS. Anvisning i brug af tilsaetningsstoffer til beton. (Advice on the use of admixtures in structural concrete.) Copenhagen, 1973.

28. AMERICAN CONCRETE INSTITUTE, Committee 212. Guide for use of admixtures in concrete. ACI Proceedings. September 1971. Volume 68, No. 9. pp. 646 - 676.

29. RILEM WORKING GROUP 'Concrete Admixtures'. Final Report. Materials and Structures. November/December 1975. No. 48. pp. 451 - 472.

30. DEUTSCHES INSTITUT FÜR NORMUNG e.V. DIN 1045. Beton und Stahlbetonbau; Bemessung und Ausführung. (Concrete and reinforced concrete structures. Design and construction.) Berlin, Beuth Verlag Gmbh, 1978.

31. BRITISH STANDARDS INSTITUTION. CP 110 : Part 1 : 1972. The structural use of concrete. Part 1. Design, materials and workmanship. pp. 154. (With Amendment AMD 2289 of May 1977.)

Table 1 Types of admixture covered by National Standard Specifications reviewed.

Types of Admixture	Symbols
Water - reducing	WR
Air - entraining	AE
Set - retarding	SRe
Set - accelerating	SAc
Accelerators of hardening *	Ac
Expansion Producing	Ex
Antifreezing	aF
Permeability - reducing	PR
Bonding	B
Colouring	C
Water - reducing and air - entraining	WR-AE
Water - reducing and set - retarding	WR-SRe
Water - reducing and set - accelerating	WR-SAc
Water - reducing accelerators of hardening	WR-Ac
Air - entraining accelerators of hardening	AE-Ac
Antifreezing accelerators of hardening	aF-Ac
Permeability - reducing and water - repelling	PR-aW
Strength-increasing	StI
Strength-increasing and set - retarding	StI-SRe
Permeability - reducing and liquid - repelling	PR-aL

* Which very often shorten the setting period

Table 2 Types of admixture covered by Standards of individual countries.

Country	WR	AE	SRe	SAc	Ac	Ex	aF	PR	B	C	WR-AE	WR-SRe	WR-SAc	WR-Ac	AE-Ac	aF-Ac	PR-aW	SfI	SfI-SRe	PR-aL
Australia	X	X	X	X	X							X	X							
Austria	X	X	X		X									X	X					
Belgium	X	X	X	X	X			X			X			X		X				
Bulgaria	X	X	X	X	X			X			X	X								
Canada	X	X	X		X							X		X						
Columbia	X	X	X	X	X							X								
France *	X	X	X	X	X	X	X		X			X					X	X	X	X
Israel	X	X	X	X								X	X							
Italy	X	X	X		X						X			X		X				
Romania	X															X				
United Kingdom	X	X	X		X					X		X		X						
USA	X	X	X		X							X		X						

* Norme Francaise, NF P 18 – 103 deals primarily with classification and marking

167

Table 3 Attributes of admixtures upon which compliance limits are placed by Standards and Regulations of individual countries. (For notes on table see page 170.)

Attribute of admixture	Country											
	Australia	Austria	Belgium	Bulgaria	Canada	France	Germany	Israel	Italy[d]	Romania	UK	USA[g]
‡* General — Physical state	X	X	X							X		
Content of particular constituents												
‡* Dry solids[a]	X		X		X	X		X	X	X	X[f]	X
* Loss on ignition[b]			X							X	X	
Insoluble residue		X	X					X	X[e]	X		
* Insoluble residue after ignition												
Moisture					X[c]							
* Reducing sugars			X			X		X	X	X		
* Chlorides												
Total			X			X	X	X	X		X	
Water soluble		X	X									
Anhydrous calcium chloride		X										
* Sulphates												
Sulphur			X									
* Nitrate and ammonia												
* Phosphate												
Sulphonated lignin									X			

*   Recommended by RILEM report[29] for adequate characterisation of an admixture

‡   Recommended by RILEM report[29] for control of the admixture itself

Table 3 Attributes of admixtures upon which compliance limits are placed by Standards and Regulations of individual countries (continued). (For notes on table see page 170.)

Attribute of admixture	Australia	Austria	Belgium	Bulgaria	Canada	France	Germany	Israel	Italy [d]	Romania	UK	USA [g]
Special properties												
* pH	X		X		X	X		X	X	X	X	
Total alkalinity									X			
* Surface tension									X			
* Foam stability												
Foam capacity									X [k]			
* Specific surface												
*⎰ Relative density	X		X		X	**X**		X	X			X
*⎱ Specific volume												
Apparent density						X [h]						
* Freezing point			X									
* Electrochemical behaviour							X					
Measurement of colour			X									
Identification												
Ŧ*⎰ Infra‑red spectra	X											X
⎸ x‑ray spectra												
⎱ x‑ray fluorescence												
UV absorption	X											
Ŧ* Check on manufacturer's methods												

*   Recommended by RILEM report (29) for adequate characterisation of an admixture

Ŧ   Recommended by RILEM report (29) for control of the admixture itself

Notes on Table 3

a. Residue at 105°C; alternatively expressed as weight loss at 105°C

b. Alternatively expressed as residue on ignition (ash)

c. For non-liquid admixtures

d. Tests called for but no limits specified

e. In distilled water and lime saturated water

f. By distilling the admixture in a carrier liquid completely immiscible with and lighter than water, and collecting and measuring the water evolved

g. When requested by purchaser in order to test admixture for uniformity or equivalence

h. For powdered admixtures

k. Only for the admixture type "Water - reducing and air - entraining"

Table 4 Types of test and reference mix for which compliance limits are imposed by Standards and Regulations of individual countries.

Admixture Type	Country											
	Australia	Austria	Belgium	Bulgaria	Canada	France	Germany	Israel	Italy	Romania *	UK	USA
WR	– – C	– – –	P – C	– – C	– – C	– M C	P – –	– – C	P M C	– – –	– – C	– – C
AE	– – C	.. – –	P – C	– – –	– – C	– M C	P – –	– – C	P M C	– – –	– – C	– M Ŧ C
SRe	– – C	– – –	– M C	P – C	– – C	– M –	– – –	– – C	P M C	– – –	– – C	– – C
Ac	– – C	P M C	– – C	P – C	– – C	– M –	– – –	– – C	P M C	– – –	– – C	– – C
PR	– – –	– – –	P – C	– – C	– – –	– – –	P – –	– – –	– – –	– – –	– – –	– – –

Note P indicates criteria for tests on paste

      M indicates criteria for tests on mortar

      C indicates criteria for tests on concrete

* The Romanian Standards [15,16] do not include performance requirements

Ŧ Optional

Table 5 Specification performance requirements relating to paste containing different types of admixture.

Property	Austria	Belgium	Germany	Germany	Italy	Italy	Italy	Italy
Country and admixture types concerned	Ac *	WR, AE and PR	WR, AE and PR	WR, AE and PR	WR	AE	SRe	Ac
Water for Standard Consistence	-	-	-	-	≤ 0.97 R	-	-	-
Setting time h : min — Initial	≥ 0 : 45 ≤ R + 1 h	≥ 0 : 45	≥ 1 h	≥ 1 h	Must comply with Standard for Cements	Must comply with Standard for Cements	≥ R + 1 : 30	≥ Cements Standard less 15 min
Setting time h : min — Final	≤ R + 1 h	≥ 3 h ≥ 12 h	< 16 h (< 12 h if to be used in prestressed concrete)	< 16 h (< 12 h if to be used in prestressed concrete)	Must comply with Standard for Cements	Must comply with Standard for Cements	≥ R + 1 : 30	Must comply with Standard for Cements
Volume Stability	Must comply with Standard for cements	Determined as for cement: spreading ≤ 6 mm‡	"Biscuit" test (i) No cracking (ii) Deflexion < 2 mm	"Biscuit" test (i) No cracking (ii) Deflexion < 2 mm	Expansion in autoclave ≤ (R + 0.10) %	Expansion in autoclave ≤ (R + 0.10) %	Expansion in autoclave ≤ (R + 0.10) %	Expansion in autoclave ≤ (R + 0.10) %

* Described in ÖNORM B 3332 as "Antifreezing"

‡ ie. spreading of indicator points

"R" represents the value of the property or characteristic concerned obtained for the reference paste.

Table 6 Specification requirements relating to mortar containing different types of admixture. (For notes on table see page 175.)

Country	Austria	Belgium	Italy				USA
Type of admixture	Ac[a]	SRe	WR	AE	SRe	Ac	AE
Water reduction	-	-	≥0.06 R	-	-	-	-
Workability (at same w/c ratio)	-	-	≥1.15 R[b]	-	-	-	-
Air content	-	-	-	≥(R + 7) %	-	-	Within range (X ± 2) %[c]
Initial Set	-	>R + 1 h	-	-	-	-	-
Heat Released	>R	-	-	-	-	-	-
Compressive and Flexural Strength	-	-	1 day: > 0.90 R at other ages: > 0.95 R	at all ages: ≥0.60 R	28 day: ≥0.95 R	1 day: ≥ 1.15 R at other ages: ≥R	-
Shrinkage	-	-	≤(R + 0.010) %		≤ (R + 0.030)%		-

173

Table 6   Specification requirements relating to mortar containing different types of admixture (continued). (For notes on table-see page 175.)

Country	France				
Type of admixture	WR	AE	SRe	Ac	PR g
Bleeding	–	–	?	–	–
Setting time h:min — Initial	at 5°C: ≥R+1:30, ≤R+3 / at 20°C: ≥R+1, ≤R+2	≥R–1, ≤R–2	≥R+1, ≤R+3 day	≥0:30, ≤R–1 } f	≥R+1, ≤R+2
Setting time h:min — Final	at 5°C: ≥R+2, ≤R+4 / at 20°C: ≥R+1:30	≥R–1:30, ≤R+3	Final less initial ≥R	Final less initial ≤R	≥R+1:30, ≤R+3
Heat of Hydration d — 6 h				≥1.50 R	
Heat of Hydration d — 12 h				≥1.30 R	
Heat of Hydration d — 1 day				≥1.05 R	
Heat of Hydration d — 5 day				≥R	
Compressive and Flexural Strength — 1 day	–	–	–	at 5°C: ≥0.20 R / at 20°C: ≥1.15 R	–
3	–	–	–	at 5°C: ≥0.50 R / at 20°C: ≥R	≥0.85 R
7	–	–	≥0.80 R	–	≥0.85 R
28	–	–	≥0.90 R	–	≥0.85 R
90	–	–	≥R	–	≥0.85 R
Shrinkage — 7 day	≤1.05 R		≤1.25 R	≤1.40 R	≤1.10 R
28	≤1.05 R		≤1.10 R	≤1.40 R	≤1.10 R
90	≤1.05 R		≤1.10 R	≤1.30 R	≤1.10 R
Capillary Absorption — 7 day age		≤R^e	–	–	≤0.50 R^e
Capillary Absorption — 90 day age		≤R^e	–	–	≤0.50 R^e

174

Notes on Table 6

a. Actually described by ÖNORM B3332 as "antifreezing"

b. Measured by flow table test

c. Optional requirement for mortars prepared from successive lots of the admixture. X is the value of air content obtained with the original acceptance sample

d. Using Langavant Calorimeter

e. Capillary absorption of mortar containing admixture must be not greater than limit given after testing for both 1 and 7 days

f. At both 5°C and 20°C

g. Actually "permeability - reducing and water - repelling"

In the table, "R" represents the value of the property or characteristic concerned obtained for the reference mortar mix.

Table 7.1 Specification performance requirments relating to non air-entrained concrete containing water-reducing admixtures. (For notes on table see page 178.)

Country	Australia	Belgium	Bulgaria	Canada	France Low C$_3$A	France High C$_3$A
Water reduction	≥ 0.05 R	≥ 0.05 R	≥ 0.05 R	≥ 0.05 R	≥15 litres ≥ 0.086 R	≥12 litres ≥ 0.069 R
Consistence (at same w/c)	-	-	-	-	-	-
Air content	-	-	-	-	at N ≤ 5% at 3N ≤ 6% } d	-
Bleeding	-	-	-	-	-	-
Setting or stiffening time, h:min — Initial	≥ R - 1 ≤ R + 1	-	-	≥ R - 1 : 20 ≤ R + 1 : 20	-	-
Setting or stiffening time, h:min — Final	≥ R - 1 ≤ R + 1	-	-	-	-	-
Compressive strength — 1 day	-	≥ 1.10 R	-	-	-	-
Compressive strength — 3	≥ 1.10 R	-	-	≥ 1.15 R/1.05 ^{a}	≥ 1.10 R	≥ 1.10 R
Compressive strength — 7	≥ 1.10 R	≥ 1.10 R	≥ 1.05 R	≥ 1.15 R/1.05	≥ 1.10 R	≥ 1.10 R
Compressive strength — 28	≥ 1.10 R	-	≥ 1.10 R	≥ 1.15 R/1.05	≥ 1.10 R	≥ 1.10 R
Compressive strength — 90	≥ R	-	-	-	≥ 1.10 R	≥ 1.10 R
Compressive strength — 180	≥ R	-	-	≥ R/1.05 } b	-	-
Compressive strength — 365	≥ R	-	-	≥ R/1.05	-	-
Tensile strength	Splitting 3, 7, 28 and 90 day ≥ R	-	-	-	Splitting 3, 7, 28 and 90 day ≥ 1.05 R	-
Shrinkage	-	-	-	(i) ≤ 1.35 R ^{c} (ii) ≤ R + 0.010%	-	-

176

Table 7.1 Specification performance requirements relating to non air-entrained concrete containing water-reducing admixtures (continued). (For notes on table see page 178.)

Country		Israel	Italy	UK	USA
Water reduction		$\geqslant 0.08$ R	$\geqslant 0.05$ R	$\geqslant 0.05$ R	$\geqslant 0.05$ R
Consistence (at same w/c)		–	$\geqslant 1.10$ R	–	–
Air content		$\leqslant$ (R + 1) %	–	$\leqslant$ (R +2) % and $\leqslant 3\%$	–
Bleeding		Capacity and duration within range R $\pm$ D e	$\leqslant 0.95$ R	–	–
Setting or stiffening time, h:min	Initial	$\geqslant$ R – 1 $\leqslant$ R + 1	–	$\geqslant$ R – 1 $\leqslant$ R + 1	$\geqslant$ R – 1 $\leqslant$ R + 1 : 30
	Final	$\geqslant$ R – 1 $\leqslant$ R + 1 }f	–	$\geqslant$ R – 1 $\leqslant$ R + 1	$\geqslant$ R – 1 $\leqslant$ R + 1 : 30
Compressive strength	1 day	$\geqslant 1.10$ R	$\geqslant 1.05$ R	–	–
	3	$\geqslant 1.10$ R	$\geqslant 1.05$ R	–	$\geqslant 1.10$ R
	7	–	$\geqslant 1.10$ R	$\geqslant 1.10$ R	$\geqslant 1.10$ R
	28	$\geqslant 1.10$ R	$\geqslant 1.15$ R	$\geqslant 1.10$ R	$\geqslant 1.10$ R } g
	90	$\geqslant 1.10$ R	$\geqslant 1.15$ R	–	–
	180	–	–	–	$\geqslant$ R
	365	–	–	–	$\geqslant$ R
Tensile strength		Flexural 28 day $\geqslant 1.05$ R	–	–	Flexural 3, 7 and 28 day $\geqslant$ R } g
Shrinkage		$\leqslant 1.20$ R at 3 months	–	–	(i) $\leqslant 1.35$ R (ii) $\leqslant$ R + 0.010 % }c

177

Notes to Table 7.1

a. 1.05 is a multiplying factor applied to the test mix strength results as an allowance for testing tolerance

b. Only at purchaser request or if no previous test or service record available.

c. If R exceeds 0.030%, limit (i) applies
   If R is not more than 0.30%, limit (ii) applies

d. N denotes normal recommended dose of WR
   3N denotes 3 x normal recommended dose of WR

e. Where D is the acceptable deviation quoted by the manufacturer, if declared

f. Not obligatory

g. No strength test result for the test mix must be less than 90% of that at any prior age; ie. it is required that the strength of the test mix does not decrease with age

In the table, "R" represents the value of the property or characteristic concerned obtained for the reference concrete mix.

Table 7.2 Specification performance requirements relating to concrete containing air-entraining admixtures. (For notes on table see page 181.)

Country		Australia [a]	Belgium	Bulgaria	Canada [a]	France
Water content		-	-	$\geq$ 0.95 R $\leq$ 1.10 R	-	-
Air content		-	$\geq$ (R + 2.5) %	-	-	at N, $\geq$ (R + 2) % at M, $\leq$ (R + 4) % $\Big\}$ k
Bleeding		$\leq$ (R + 2) %	-	-	-	-
Setting or stiffening time, h:min	Initial	$\geq$ R − 1 $\leq$ R + 1	-	-	$\geq$ R − 1 $\leq$ R + 1	-
	Final	$\geq$ R − 1 $\leq$ R + 1	-	-	-	-
Compressive strength	1 day	-	$\geq$ R− 4 A_t $\big\}$ b		-	-
	3	-	-		$\geq$ R/1.05 [c]	$\geq$ 0.80 R
	7	$\geq$ 0.90 R	$\geq$ R− 4 A_t	$\geq$ 0.90 R (age unspecified)	$\geq$ R/1.05	$\geq$ 0.80 R
	28	$\geq$ 0.90 R	-		$\geq$ R/1.05	$\geq$ 0.80 R
	90	$\geq$ 0.90 R	-		-	$\geq$ 0.80 R
	180	-	-		$\geq$ R/1.05 $\Big\}$ d	-
	365	$\geq$ 0.90 R	-		$\geq$ R/1.05	-
Tensile Strength		-	-	-	-	Splitting 3, 7, 28 and 90 day $\geq$ 0.80 R
Shrinkage		-	-	-	(i) $\leq$ 1.20 R (ii) $\leq$ R + 0.006 % $\Big\}$ e	-
Freeze-thaw Resistance		-	-	$\geq$ R + "1 grade"	AVSF $\leq$ 200 um $\big\}$ f, g or RDF $\geq$ R/1.10	(i) Strength $\geq$ 0.70 R (ii) Ed $\geq$ 50 % $\Big\}$ m

179

Table 7.2 Specification performance requirements relating to concrete containing air-entraining admixtures (continued). For notes on table see page 181.

Country		Israel	Italy	UK[r]	USA[a]
Water content		≤ 0.92 R	-	-	-
Air content		≥ (R + 4) % ≤ (R + 6) %	≥ (R + 3) %	Repeatability[s] 4 % ≤ A ≤ 6 %	-
Bleeding		Capacity and duration within range $R \pm D$[n]	≤ (R - 5) %	≤	≤ (R + 2) %
Setting or stiffening time, h:min	Initial	≥ R - 1 ≤ R + 1:30	-	≥ R - 1 ≤ R + 1	≥ R - 1:15 ≤ R + 1:15
	Final	≥ R - 1 ≤ R + 1:30 }[p]	-	≥ R - 1 ≤ R + 1	≥ R - 1:15 ≤ R + 1:15
Compressive strength	1 day	≥ 0.75 R	≥ 0.90 R at all ages	-	≥ 0.90 R at any age
	3	≥ 0.85 R		-	
	7	-		-	
	28	≥ 0.85 R		≥ 0.70 R	
	90	≥ 0.85 R		-	
	180	-		-	
	365	-		-	
Tensile strength		Flexural 28 day ≥ 0.85 R	-	-	≥ 0.90 R[u] at any age
Shrinkage		≤ 1.20 R at 3 months	-	-	(i) ≤ 1.20 R (ii) ≤ R + 0.005 % }[e,u]
Freeze-thaw resistance		-	DF ≥ 1.30 R[q]	$\dfrac{l_{50} - l_0}{l_0} \leq 0.0005$[t]	RDF ≥ 80 %[v]

Notes to Table **7**.2

a. Reference mix contains a reference air-entraining agent (neutralized Vinsol resin)

b. A_t is the additional air content, %, in excess of that of the reference mix

c. 1.05 is a multiplying factor applied to the test mix strength results as an allowance for testing tolerance

d. Only at purchaser's request or if no previous test or service record available

e. If R exceeds 0.030%, limit (i) applies
   If R is not more than 0.030%, limit (ii) applies

f. At purchaser's option either air-void spacing factor (ASTM C457) or relative durability factor (ASTM C666, Procedure A) may be used to determine durability

g. 1.10 is a correction factor included as an allowance for testing tolerance

k. N denotes normal recommended dose of AE
   M denotes maximum recommended dose of AE

m. After 90 cycles between $-16^{\circ}C$ and $5^{\circ}C$
   (i) test mix flexural and compressive strength are compared with those of test mix prisms not subjected to freeze-thaw cycles

   and

   (ii) dynamic modulus is compared with initial dynamic modulus before freezing and thawing

n. Where D is the acceptable deviation quoted by the manufacturer, if declared

p. Not obligatory

q. To UNI 7087 - 72

r. Draft standard

s. 'A' indicates individual air contents for three consecutive test mix batches determined by one operator using one set of equipment

t. Relative length change after 50 cycles between $-15^{\circ}C$ and $16^{\circ}C$

u. Applicable only when specifically required by purchaser for structures where flexural strength or volume change may be critically important

v. Relative durability factor of test mix after freeze-thaw cycling from $-17.8^{\circ}C$ to $4.4.^{\circ}C$ (ASTM C666)

In the table, "R" represents the value of the property or characteristic concerned obtained for the reference concrete mix.

Table 7.3   Specification performance requirements relating to non air-entrained concrete containing set-retarding admixtures. (For notes on table see page 184.)

Country		Australia	Belgium	Bulgaria	Canada
Water content		–	–	–	≤ 0.97 R
Air Content		–	–	–	–
Bleeding		–	–	–	–
Setting or stiffening time, h:min	Initial	≥ R + 1 ≤ R + 3	–	–	≥ R + 1 ≤ R + 3
	Final	≥ R + 1 ≤ R + 3	–	–	–
Compressive strength	1 day	–	–	–	–
	3	≥ 0.90 R	≥ 0.90 R ^{a}	–	> 1.15 R/1.05 ^{b}
	7	≥ 0.90 R	–	–	> 1.15 R/1.05
	28	≥ R	≥ R ^{a}	≥ R	> 1.15 R/1.05
	90	≥ R	–	–	–
	180	≥ R	–	–	> R/1.05
	365	≥ R	–	–	> R/1.05 } ^{c}
Tensile strength		Splitting 3 and 7 day ≥ 0.90 R 28 and 90 day > R	–	–	–
Shrinkage		–	–	–	(i) ≤ 1.35 R (ii) ≤ R + 0.010 % } ^{d}

182

Table 7.3 Specification performance requirements relating to non air-entrained concrete containing set-retarding admixtures (continued). (For notes on table see page 184.)

Country	France [e]	Israel	Italy	UK	USA
Water content	–	–	–	–	–
Air content	–	≤ (R + 1) %	–	≤ (R + 2) % and ≤ 3 %	–
Bleeding	–	Capacity and duration within range k ± D [f]	–	–	–
Setting or stiffening time, h:min — Initial	–	≥ R + 1 : 30	≥ R + 0 : 45	≥ R + 1	≥ R + 1 ≤ R + 3 : 30
Setting or stiffening time, h:min — Final	–	≤ R + 4	≥ R + 0 : 45	–	≤ R + 3 : 30
Compressive strength — 1 day	–	–	–	–	≥ 0.90 R
Compressive strength — 3	–	≥ 0.90 R	–	–	≥ 0.90 R
Compressive strength — 7	–	≥ R	–	≥ 0.90 R	≥ 0.90 R
Compressive strength — 28	–	≥ R	–	≥ 0.95 R	≥ 0.90 R
Compressive strength — 90	–	≥ R	≥ R	–	≥ 0.90 R [h]
Compressive strength — 180	–	–	–	–	≥ 0.90 R [h]
Compressive strength — 365	–	–	–	–	≥ 0.90 R } [g]
Tensile strength	–	Flexural 28 day ≥ 0.90 R	–	–	Flexural 3, 7 & 28 day ≥ 0.90 R } [g]
Shrinkage	–	≤ 1.20 R at 3 months	–	–	(i) ≤ 1.35 R (ii) ≤ R + 0.010 % } [d]

183

<u>Notes to Table 7.3</u>

a. At both 20°C and 30°C

b. 1.05 is a multiplying factor applied to the test mix strength results as an allowance for testing tolerance

c. Only at purchaser's request, or if no previous test or service record available

d. If Rexceeds 0.030%, limit (i) applies
    If R is not more than 0.030%, limit (ii) applies

e. COPLA criteria for approval of set-retarding admixtures do not include performance requirements for concrete test mixes.

f. Where D is the acceptable deviation quoted by the manufacturer, if declared

g. No strength test result for the test mix must be less than 90% of that at any prior age; ie. it is required that the strength of the test mix does not decrease with age

h. When the admixture is tested for use in specific work the tests at 6 months and 1 year may be waived

In the table, "R" represents the value of the property or characteristi.

concerned obtained for the reference concrete mix.

Table 7.4 Specification performance requirements relating to non air-entrained concrete containing accelerators of hardening. (For notes on table see page 187.)

Country	Australia	Austria	Belgium	Bulgaria	Canada
Water content	–	–	–	–	≤ R
Air content	–	–	–	–	–
Bleeding	–	–	–	–	–
Setting or stiffening time, h:min — Initial	≥ R − 3 ≤ R − 1	–	–	–	≥ R − 1 ≤ R − 3
Setting or stiffening time, h:min — Final	≥ R − 3 ≤ R − 1	–	–	–	–
Compressive strength — 1 day	–	–	at 20°C ≥ 1.25 R	≥ 1.15 R	≥ 1.25 R/1.05 a
Compressive strength — 3	≥ 1.25 R	–	at 5°C ≥ 1.25 R	≥ 1.15 R	≥ 1.10 R/1.05
Compressive strength — 7	≥ R	≥ 0.90 R	at 5° and 20°C ≥ R	≥ 1.10 R	≥ R
Compressive strength — 28	≥ R	–	–	–	≥ R/1.05
Compressive strength — 90	≥ R	–	–	–	≥ R/1.05 } b
Compressive strength — 180	–	–	–	–	–
Compressive strength — 365	≥ R	–	–	–	–
Tensile strength	Splitting 3 day ≥ 1.10 R 7, 28 and 90 day ≥ R	–	–	–	–
Shrinkage	–	≤ 2 R at 90 days	–	–	(i) ≤ 1.35 R (ii) ≤ R + 0.010 % } c

Table 7.4 Specification performance requirements relating to non air-entrained concrete containing accelerators of hardening (continued). (For notes on table see page 187.)

Country	France [d]	Israel	Italy	UK	USA
Water content	–	–	–	–	–
Air content	–	$\leq (R+1)$ %	–	$\leq (R+2)$ % and $< 3\%$	–
Bleeding	–	Capacity and duration within range $R \pm D$ [e]	–	–	–
Setting or stiffening time, h:min — Initial	–	$\geq R - 3:30$ / $\leq R - 1$	$\leq R - 0:30$	>1	$\leq R - 1$ / $\geq R - 3:30$
Setting or stiffening time, h:min — Final	–	$\geq R - 3:30$ / $\leq R - 1$	$\leq R - 0:30$	$\geq R - 1$	$\leq R - 1$
Compressive strength — 1 day	–	$\geq 1.50\,R$	$\geq 1.15\,R$	$\geq 1.25\,R$	–
Compressive strength — 3	–	$\geq 1.25\,R$	$\geq 1.15\,R$	–	$\geq 1.25\,R$
Compressive strength — 7	–	–	Also $\geq R$ at later standard ages of test for cement used	$\geq R$	$\geq R$ [f]
Compressive strength — 28	–	$\geq R$		$\geq R$	$\geq R$
Compressive strength — 90	–	$\geq R$		–	–
Compressive strength — 180	–	–		–	$\geq 0.90\,R$ [g]
Compressive strength — 365	–	–		–	$\geq 0.90\,R$ [g]
Tensile strength	–	Flexural 28 day $> R$	–	–	Flexural 3 day $> 1.10\,R$ / 7 day $> R$ / 28 day $> 0.90\,R$ [f]
Shrinkage	–	$\leq 1.20\,R$ at 90 days	–	–	(i) $\leq 1.35\,R$ / (ii) $\leq R + 0.010\%$ [c]

186

Notes to Table 7.4

a.   1.05 is a multiplying factor applied to the test mix strength results as an allowance for testing tolerance

b.   Only at purchaser's request or if no previous test or service record available

c.   If R exceeds 0.030%, limit (i) applies
     If R is not more than 0.030%, limit (ii) applies

d.   COPLA criteria for approval of accelerators of hardening do not include performance requirements for concrete test mixes

e.   Where D is the acceptable deviation quoted by the manufacturer, if declared

f.   No strength test result for the test mix must be less than 90% of that at any prior age; ie. it is required that the strength of the test mix does not decrease with age

g.   When the admixture is tested for use in specific work, the tests at 6 months and 1 year may be waived

In the table, "R" represents the value of the property or characteristic

concerned obtained for the reference concrete mix.

Table 7.5 Specification performance requirements relating to concrete containing permeability-reducing admixtures.

Country	Belgium	Bulgaria	France [a]
Water reduction	−	$\geqslant$ 0.05 R	−
Air content	−	−	at N, $\leqslant (R + 6)\%$ at M or 3N, $\leqslant (R + 8)\%$ [b]
Strength	$\geqslant$ 0.90 R at any age	−	−
Water-tightness	−	$\geqslant$ R + 10^5 pa	

Notes

a. The admixture type described as "Hydrofuge" in Norme Francaise NF P 18 - 103 is "Permeability-reducing and water-repelling".

b. N denotes manafacturer's normal recommended dose.
M denotes manufacturer's maximum recommended dose.

In the table, "R" represents the value of the property or characteristic concerned obtained for the reference concrete mix.

The use of admixtures in concrete pressure vessels for nuclear plant

R Blundell and R D Browne
Taylor Woodrow Research Laboratories, UK

INTRODUCTION

In April 1962 construction of the first two U.K. prestressed concrete pressure vessels for nuclear reactor containment began at Oldbury
on the South bank of the Severn estuary. Approximately 36,000 cubic
metres of high strength concrete were produced with a mean 28 day
strength of $51N/mm^2$ and a standard deviation of $4.1N/mm^2$. All the
concrete used in the construction of the pressure vessels contained a
lignosulphonate based non-retarding water reducing admixture added at
the rate of 180ml per 50kg of Sulphate Resisting Cement [1].

Since the construction of the two vessels at Oldbury, a total of
twelve further P.C.P.V.'s have been construction at the following
Nuclear Power Stations:-

> Wylfa, Anglesey
> Dungeness B, Kent
> Hinkley Point B, Ayrshire
> Hartlepool, Teeside
> Heysham, Lancashire

Approximately one quarter of a million cubic metres of concrete has
beenplaced in these structures, all of which contained a lignosulphonate
workability aid.

It will be appreciated that nuclear structures, and in particular
the containment system for the nuclear reactor itself, are subject to
stringent quality assurance and safety checking procedures. Before
materials can be used in the construction of the pressure vessels they
have to be shown to be capable of performing satisfactorily under the
arduous operating conditions which will exist throughout the vessels
design life of 30 years.

The authors have been intimately involved in the extensive programmes of material selection and concrete property testing for the
P.C.P.V.'s at Wylfa, Hartlepool and Heysham and are currently under-
taking a comprehensive programme of concrete property tests for the
latest two A.G.R. power stations to be sited at Torness and Heysham.

This paper summarises the work undertaken in connection with these
structures which included extensive testing of the proposed construction materials after exposure to severe levels of neutron and
gamma irradiation.

All the concrete tested in the authors laboratories, on site and
in the U.K.A.E.A. Herald Reactor at Culcheth contained the proposed
admixture which under the conditions of test examined caused no detrimental effect to the physical properties of the hardened concrete
whilst their use enabled workable mixes to be designed utilising
crushed rock aggregates and low water cement ratios without recause to
excessively high cement contents.

TEST WORK UNDERTAKEN

To accurately establish the behaviour of the concrete to be
used in the P.C.P.V.'s at Wylfa, Hartlepool and Heysham comprehensive
test programmes were undertaken to determine the physical properties of
the concretes under realistic operating conditions.

For the three concretes tested, over two hundred and fifty test
specimens were cast to establish the following physical properties:-

(1) Elastic and creep deformation under load.

(2) Shrinkage.

(3) Compressive strength.

(4) Thermal Expansion.

(5) Thermal Conductivity.

Detailed descriptions of the various test procedures etc. have been well
published elsewhere [2,3,4]. However, one of the principal objectives
of the programmes was to provide the vessel designer with property
data capable of being applied over the full range of operating conditions envisaged, this having been determined on test specimens
manufactured from the actual materials proposed for use on site. Details
of the P.C.P.V. mixes used at the three stations are given in Table 1.
All the specimens were subject to a mass concrete curing regime which
included subjecting them to an imposed heat of hydration cycle during

the first four days or so after casting and sealing them in butyl rubber jackets to prevent moisture movement during both curing and subsequent testing. Fig. 1 shows a typical test arrangement for one of the creep specimens.

Tests were undertaken at temperatures of 20, 40, 65 and 95°C at ages of loading of 7, 14, 40, 100, 180 and 400 days and $12\frac{1}{2}$ years.

To assess the validity of the data obtained from the laboratory programme in relation to the site produced concrete and to obtain a measure of variability of the site concrete, approximately seventy five test specimens were cast during the construction of each vessel. A further check on insitu performance compared with predicted behaviour based upon the original laboratory test programme data was obtained from measurements taken of the strains induced in the pressure vessels during prestressing, proof pressure test and finally operation [5]. This structural performance data was obtained from the 300 to 400 Vibrating Wire Strain Gauges cast into each vessel.

As mentioned earlier in addition to the physical property test work described above a comprehensive programme of tests were undertaken on samples of both the aggregates and concrete mixes to be used following exposure to high levels of gamma and neutron irradiation. Recommendations for the range of properties and materials to be examined were provided by R.D. Browne, in association with others, and the test programme was undertaken by the U.K.A.E.A. at their Culcheth laboratory [6,7].

The properties examined included:-

(a) Tensile strength.

(b) Volume change with time.

(c) Elastic and creep deformation.

(d) Gas evolution.

The maximum levels of irradiation covered in this programme were 4×10^{19} n/cm^2 integrated neutron dose and a gamma flux of 10^8 rads/hour. To obtain the above neutron dose over the experimental period high dose rates were necessary and in certain cases these were up to 120 times those likely to occur in practice.

SPECIAL TOP CAP CONCRETE

The top cap region of the pressure vessels contains up to 170 vertical penetrations through which the uranium fuel rods and reactor control rods are passed (Fig. 2). As a result, the top cap disc is a highly congested inaccessible region and hence a very workable mix is required. For Hartlepool and Heysham it was proposed to cast the top cap plugs in a single 300m^3 pour via a working platform which had to be mounted approximately 3 metres above the finished concrete level (Fig. 3) [8]. The details of the mix finally designed for this operation are given in Table 2. The strength achieved was 55N/mm^2 at 56 days and the slump was in excess of 150mm. A low heat of hydration temperature rise was required and this was achieved by using a 50:50 blend of S.R.P.C. and G.B.S.* The high slump and strength was achieved by a double dose of a low sugar content lignosulphonate workability aid. The particular admixture used was selected following laboratory testing of over twenty admixtures commercially available at this time. The admixture used was selected as it had a sugar content of less than 1.0% (this value was subsequently confirmed by tests on the material supplied to site) and as a result over-dosing by up to 3 times the normally recommended dose caused little retardation to the stiffening time. It is worth noting that some of the other admixtures tested had sugar contents of as high as 5% and as a result, even at the normally recommended dose their use caused some retardation.

The physical properties of the special top cap mix had to be determined in a similar manner to that employed on the main P.V. mixes.

TEST RESULTS

It is not intended here to re-present the results obtained from these extensive programmes of work as they have been published elsewhere [2,3,4] but to summarise the data so as to establish whether the use of the admixtures caused any significant changes to the physical properties of the concrete. In this respect the long term data now available, particularly from the Wylfa programme, is of value in establishing whether any slow acting deterioration process has occurred.

To establish whether the use of the admixture has resulted in deterioration in long term behaviour it is desirable to have a non-admixtured concrete against which to compare performance. Whilst no such mixes were cast as part of the laboratory test programmes, this objective has been achieved by comparing the results obtained with those from other non-admixtured concrete referred to in the litera-

---

* Ground Granulated Blastfurnace Slag marketed by the Frodingham Cement
  Company as Cemsave.

ture [9,10,11]. The contribution of the admixture to the concrete's performance under irradiation has been obtained from a detailed analysis of the reaction products and deterioration processes observed.

CONCRETE STRENGTH

Compressive strength measurements have been made on samples of pressure vessel concrete for periods up to 14 years from casting [12]. Fig. 4 summarises the results of these tests where they are compared with 50 year data on concretes without admixtures [13].

As can be seen the relatively modern Pressure Vessel mixes show a substantially greater increase in strength over the first seven days or so from casting compared with 50 year old concrete. This is almost certainly due to the finer grinding and higher C_3S content present in modern cements. The presence of the admixtures, however, may also have had an effect on the early rate of strength gain by breaking up the cement agglomerates and as a result exposing a greater surface area of the cement grains for hydration. Beyond seven days the rate of strength gain of the P.V. mixes compares well with that obtained from the older non-admixtured concrete. The results indicate that over the 14 year test period the admixtures used have had no detrimental effect on strength gain.

This result is further confirmed by a series of tests carried out on samples of the Wylfa P.V. concrete summarised in Fig. 5. Here samples of concrete were heated at ages between 7 and 180 days to temperatures of either 40, 65 or 93.5°C where they remained for a period of approximately 6 years. As can be seen prolonged exposure to elevated temperature has caused no reduction in strength when related to 20°C control specimens. This is particularly gratifying for it has been well established that heating limestone aggregate concrete causes an immediate loss in strength of as much as 40% [14], Fig. 6. Therefore prolonged exposure to temperature has caused this strength loss to be fully recovered. Certainly the use of the admixture appears to have had no deleterious affect on strength which exposure to elevated temperature might have been expected to accelerate.

ELASTIC AND CREEP DEFORMATION

Figs. 7 and 8 summarise the deformation results obtained from the creep tests on the Hartlepool, Heysham and Wylfa P.V. concretes. The elastic strains induced in the concrete during loading and the subsequent creep strains have been plotted against stress/strength ratio. Also included in the Figures are the results obtained from other similarly cured concretes both with and without admixtures [9,10,11].

As can be seen the use of the admixture in moisture stable mass concrete would appear not to have increased the elastic or creep deformation underload even at elevated temperatures up to 95°C. Work has been published, however, which has shown that for concrete which is permitted to dry whilst under load the use of an admixture will increase both the creep deformation and the drying shrinkage. Fig. 9 presents the results of Hope et. al. [15] indicating the extent to which both lignosulphonate and carboxylic acid admixtures can increase the creep of drying concrete. Work published by Morgan [16] has shown that admixtures cause a similar increase in the drying shrinkage of concrete and that this is due not to an increased rate of drying but a greater shrinkage for a given loss of water. Certain of Morgans results are summarised in Figs. 10 and 11. It would seem therefore that the presence of the admixture changes the structure of the cement gel such that it becomes more creep and shrinkage sensitive under drying conditions.

However, in the moisture stable environment of the mass concrete pressure vessel moisture changes are restricted to concrete adjacent to exposed surfaces and as a result the drying effect is not significant.

It is also worth noting that even under drying conditions the use of a workability aid is likely to cause little increase in creep or shrinkage as one of the results of their use is to reduce the paste content in the mix and hence lower the proneness of the concrete to deform either under the action of stress or moisture loss.

IRRADIATION BEHAVIOUR

Concrete when subject to high levels of nuclear irradiation under-goes two major changes [17]:-

(a) A substantial growth which occurs as a result of atomic displacements in the aggregate particles caused by the fast neutrons.

(b) Radiolysis of the mix water by gamma rays which increases both creep and shrinkage and results in the evolution of gases.

The effect of these two changes is to modify the physical properties of the concrete. For example the strength and modulus of elasticity are substantially reduced not only as a result of change to the physical properties of the aggregate but also due to the high stresses generated at the aggregate/cement paste interface as a result of the former expansion and the latter shrinkage caused by the water loss.

In Pressure Vessel Design maximum integrated neutron doses are controlled below $0.5 \times 10^{18} \text{m/cm}^2$ [17] almost two orders of magnitude less than the maximum value covered in the U.K.A.E.A. programme. However, even under the severe levels of irradiation covered in the test programme the U.K.A.E.A. were able to conclude that "the various admixtures used in these materials" (the concretes and cement grouts used in the tests) "appear to have had an insignificant effect on the irradiation behaviour" [7].

SUMMARY

On the basis of the considerable test data available to date, certain of which has been summarised in this paper, it would seem that the use of lignosulphonate type admixtures have no detrimental effect on the long term properties of Pressure Vessel Concrete.

In fact, their use has contributed toward the production of workable mixes capable of being successfully placed in the congested environment of the pressure vessel whilst maintaining high levels of strength and acceptable cement contents.

REFERENCES

1. A. HOUGHTON-BROWN
   A.J. DARTON
   The Oldbury Vessels, Paper 1. Conference on P.C.P.V.'s, I.C.E. London 1968.

2. R.D. BROWNE
   Properties of Concrete in Reactor Vessels. Group C, Paper 13, Conference on P.C.P.V.'s I.C.E. London 1968.

3. R.D. BROWNE
   R. BLUNDELL
   The Behaviour of Concrete in Prestressed Concrete Pressure Vessels. 1st International Conference on Struct. Mech. in Reactor Tech., Berlin, September 1971.

4. R.D. BROWNE
   R.E.D. BURROW
   An Example of the Utilisation of Complex Multiphase Material Behaviour in Engineering Design. Paper 104, Southampton Conference on Civil Engineering Materials, 1969.

5. R.D. BROWNE
    P.B. BAMFORTH
    A.K. WELCH

The Value of Instrumentation in the Assessment of Vessel Performance during Construction and Service. Conference on P.C.P.V.'s and Containments, Int. Mech. Engs., York, September 1975.

6. B.T. KELLY et. al.

The Effects of Reactor Radiation on Concrete. Proc. 2nd Conference on P.C.P.V.'s and their Thermal Insulation, Brussels, November 1969.

7. B.S. GRAM et. al.

The Behaviour of Hardened Cement Pastes and Cement Grouts under the Influence of Reactor Irradiation. Proc. Information Exchange Mtg. on the Results of Concrete Irradiation Programmes. Brussels, April 1977. Euratom Report, EUR4751.

8. R. BLUNDELL
    R.D. BROWNE

Large Pours in Pressure Vessels. Conference on P.C.P.V.'s and Containments, Int. Mech. Engs., York, September 1975.

9. S. STÖCKL

Strengths of Concrete under Uniaxial sustained Loading. A.C.I. Conference on Concrete for Nuclear Reactors. Berlin, October 1970.

10. E. CRISPINO

Studies on the Technology of Concrete under Thermal Conditions. A.C.I. Conference on Concrete for Nuclear Reactors

11. D.J. HANNANT

Strain Behaviour of Concrete up to $95^{o}C$ under Compressive Stresses. Conference on P.C.P.V.'s, London 1967.

12. A.P. MEARS

Long Term Tests on the Effect of Moderate Heating on the Compressive Strength and Dynamic Modulus of Elasticity of Concrete. Paper SP 34-20 Concrete for Nuclear Reactors, Vol. 1., A.C.I. Publication.

13. G.W. WASHA
    K.F. WENDT

Fifty year Properties of Concrete. A.C.I. Journal, January 1975.

14. R. BLUNDELL
    C. DIMOND
    R.D. BROWNE

Thermal Stresses in Oil Storage Vessels. The Properties of Concrete for use in Design. C.I.R.I.A. U.E.G. Tech Note No. 9, October 1975.

15. B.B. HOPE   Influence of Admixtures on Creep of Con-
    A.M. NEVILLE   crete containing Normal Weight Aggregate.
    A. GURUSWAMI   RILEM Symposium on Admixtures for Mortar
                and Concrete. Brussels, September 1967.

16. D.R. MORGAN   The Effects of Lignosulphonate Based
                Admixtures on Drying Shrinkage of Con-
                crete Paste and Concrete. 1st Australian
                Conference on Engineering Materials.
                Univ. of New South Wales, 1974.

17. BRITISH STANDARD   Prestressed Concrete Pressure Vessels for
    INSTITUTION   Nuclear Reactors, BS4975, July 1973.

Table 1 Pressure vessel concrete mix proportions.

	WYLFA kg/m^3	HARTLEPOOL kg/m^3	HEYSHAM kg/m^3
Ordinary Portland Cement	400	418	435
Coarse Aggregate (40mm–5mm)	1206	1266	1186
Fine Aggregate	585	623	618
Water	168	205	191
Admixture (litres/m^3)	1.1	1.2	1.2

Coarse Aggregate Type.

      Wylfa – Crushed foraminiferal limestone.

      Hartlepool }
      Heysham   } Crushed quartz dolerite.

The admixture was of the lignosulphonate type in each case.

Table 2 Hartlepool PV top cap concrete mix proportions.

	kg/m^3
Ordinary Portland Cement	212
Ground Blastfurnace Slag	212
Crushed Dolerite Coarse Aggregate (20mm–5mm)	1168
Zone II Glacial Drift Sand	698
Water	191
Lignosulphonate Admixture (litres/m^3)	2.4

Figure 1   A typical creep specimen.

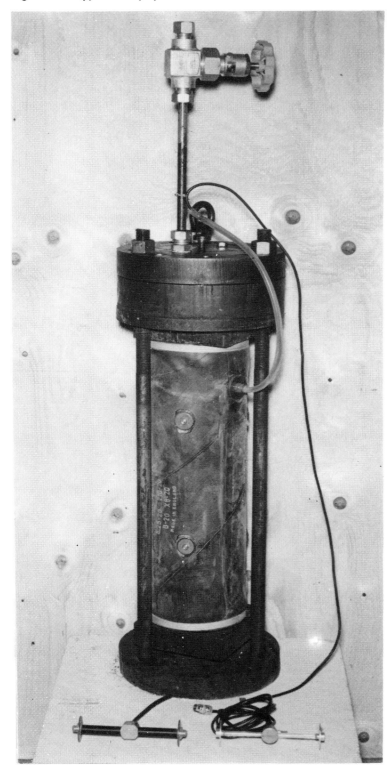

Hydraulic loading
head

Butyl Rubber
Sealing Jacket

Vibrating Wire Embedded Strain Gauges

Figure 2 Hartlepool PVI top cap plug.

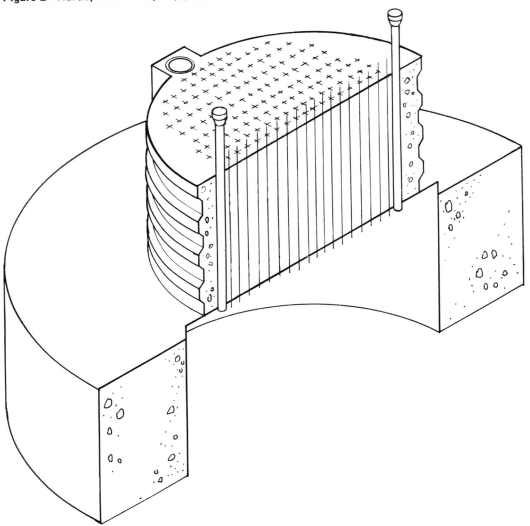

Figure 3   Casting the Hartlepool PV top cap.

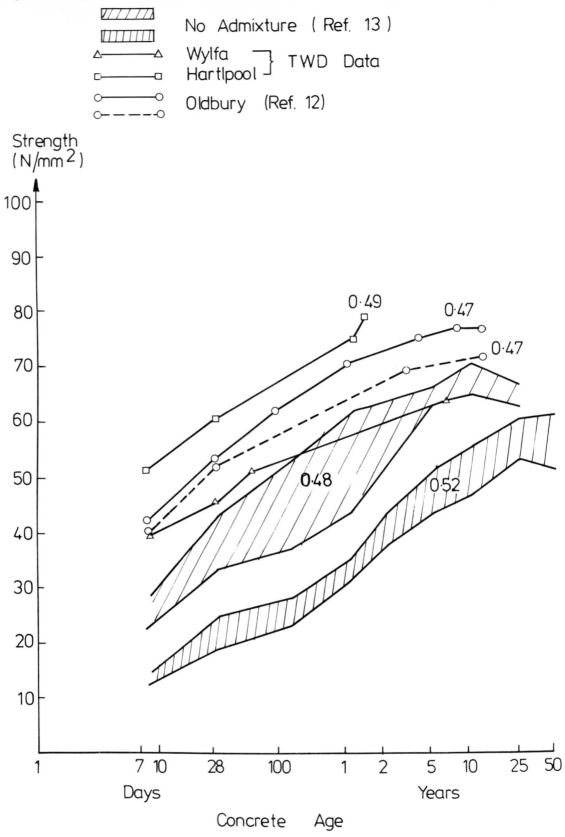

Figure 4   Long-term compressive strength development.

Figure 5   Strength of concrete after 6 years' temperature storage (Wylfa limestone aggregate).

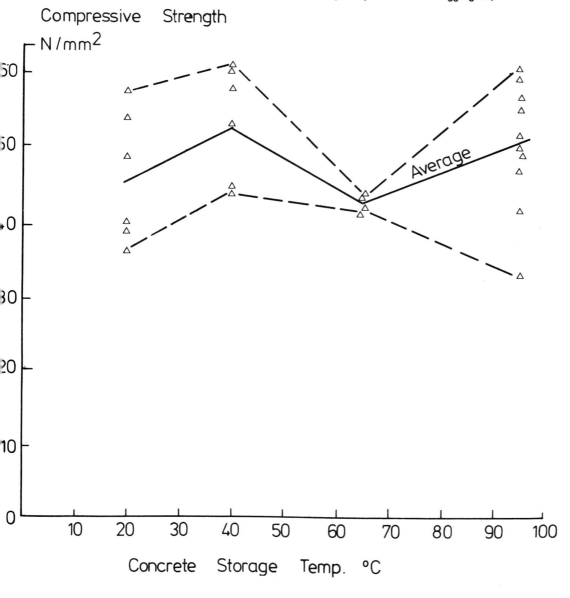

Figure 6 Concrete strength reduction at heating (Ref 14).

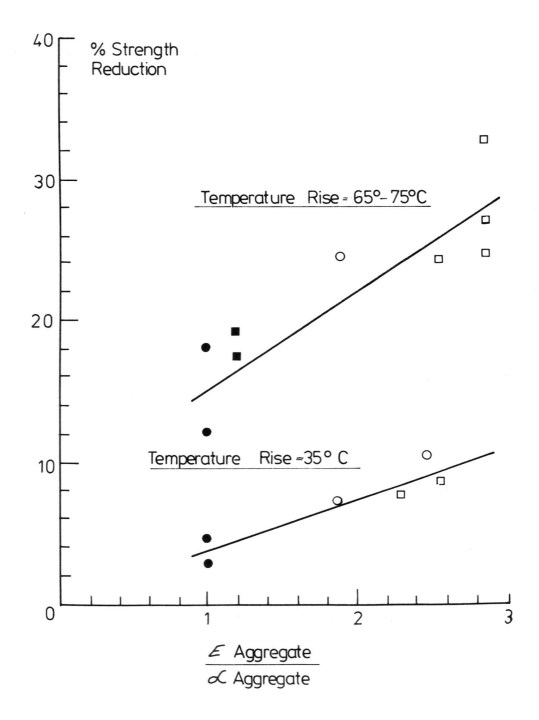

Figure 7 **The elastic deformation of concrete (TWA data + Refs 9, 10, 11).**

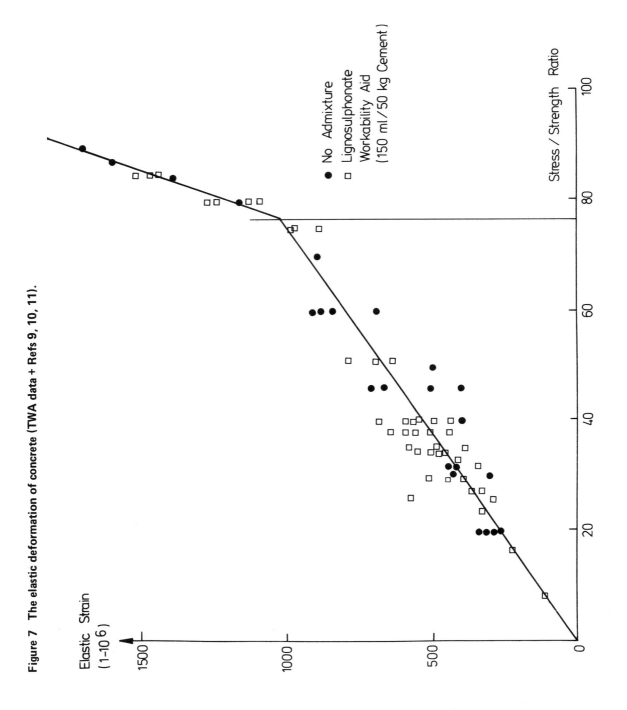

Figure 8 Creep of concrete (TWA data + Refs 9, 10, 11; time under load = 100 days).

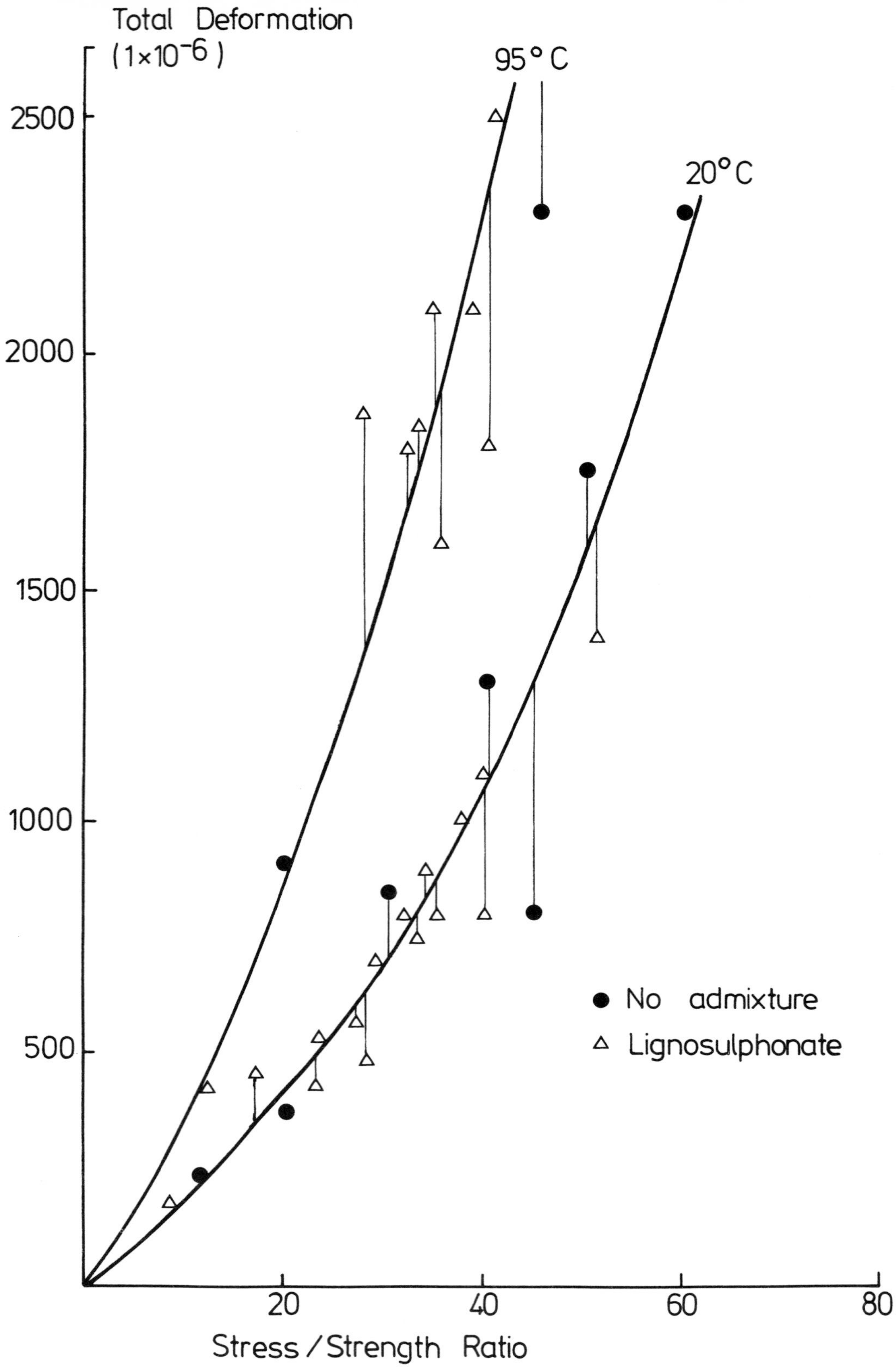

Figure 9 Creep of concrete under drying conditions (Ref 15).

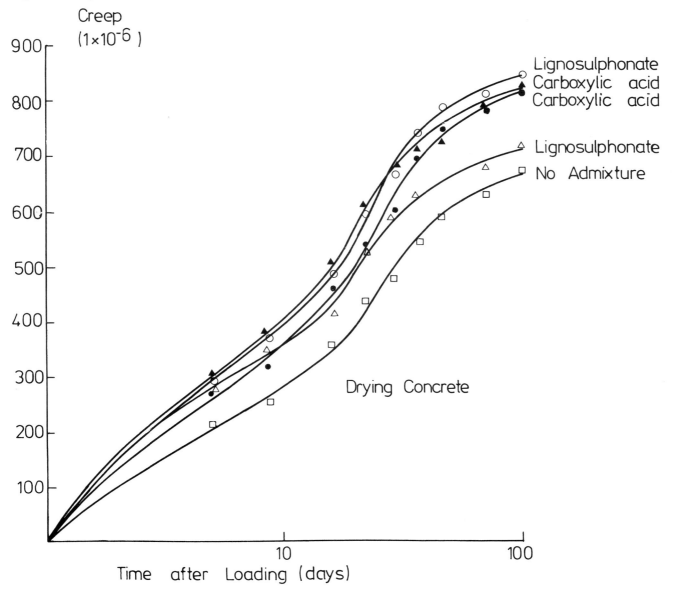

Figure 10   Shrinkage of concrete at constant workability (Ref 16).

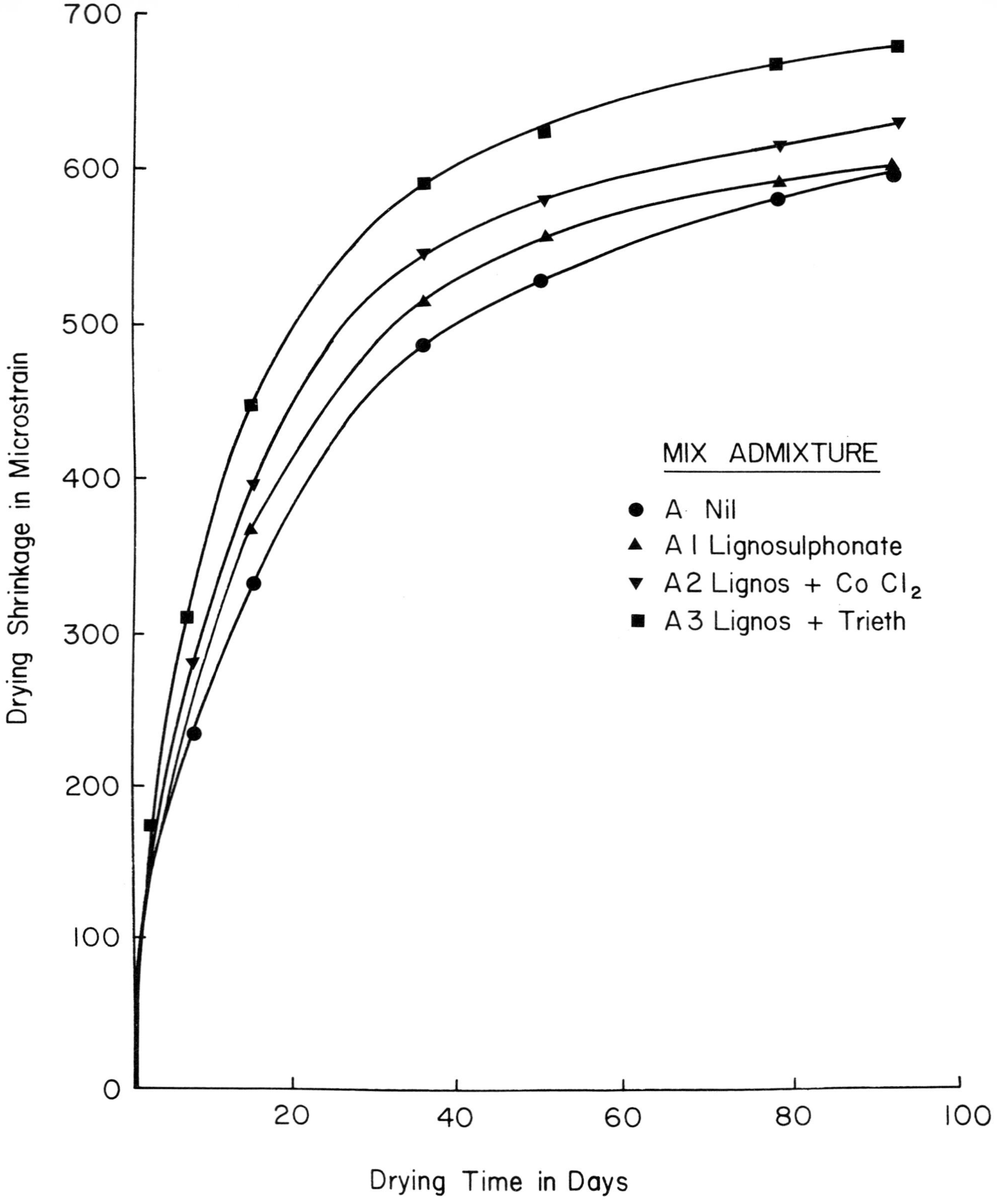

MIX   ADMIXTURE

● A Nil
▲ A I Lignosulphonate
▼ A2 Lignos + Co Cl$_2$
■ A 3 Lignos + Trieth

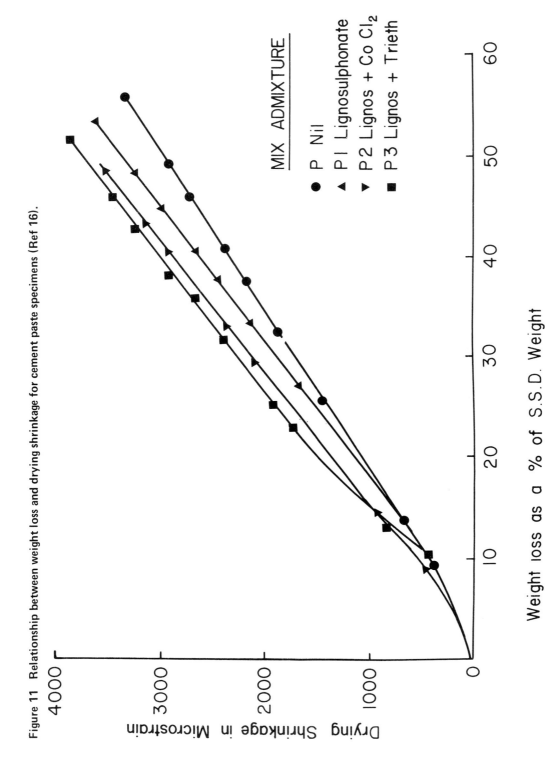

Figure 11 Relationship between weight loss and drying shrinkage for cement paste specimens (Ref 16).

MIX ADMIXTURE

● P Nil
▲ P1 Lignosulphonate
▼ P2 Lignos + Co Cl$_2$
■ P3 Lignos + Trieth

Weight loss as a % of S.S.D. Weight

Drying Shrinkage in Microstrain

General discussion

MATERIALS AND PERFORMANCE

DR N TENOUTASSE (University of Brussels, Belgium):

Professor Kreijger talked about the forming of ettringite during cement hydration.   Generally ettringite is a crystalline product.   We know that in cement hydration two hydrates will crystallize: ettringite and some other sulphoaluminate compounds, also calcium hydroxide.   But probably some other gel-like hydrates, especially tobermorite, have some role in rheology especially during initial cement hydration.

My second comment concerns the probable action of admixtures and the formation of ettringite, for which I believe we have little experimental proof.   Ettringite is generally made in a solution, and the admixture interferes with the reaction of gypsum with C_3A.   I do not think this is so with dispersing admixtures.   With some other admixtures, however, like sugar, calcium chloride and especially calcium formate or admixtures of this type, they have a very important effect on the kinetics of reaction between C_3A and gypsum.   Probably it is more a question of the cement and kinetic effects.

PROFESSOR P C KREIJGER (Technische Hogeschool, Eindhoven, The Netherlands):
This would go far beyond the scope of what I have been trying to discuss.
Dr Double, in his paper, has said something about ettringite layers, and we can leave it to him to answer the question more fundamentally in due course.

J FIGG (Harry Stanger Limited, UK):

One of the theories on freezing and thawing has suggested that the problem is partly due to orientation of molecular water, and the loss of the random array of the liquid water that is normally present in concrete. I have certainly found that the absorption of microwave changes dramatically when concrete has been frozen. Whether the water was there as solid ice I do not know, but ice itself behaves in this same way, with a very low absorption of microwave energy.

I wonder whether Dr Page's curious artefacts of these little calcium hydroxide crystals and their random well-spaced distribution in the cavities could in any way be associated with the change in the state of water. I do not know whether Dr Page mentions this in his text, but he may like to say something on this as well.

DR C L PAGE(University of Aston, Birmingham, UK):

That certainly raises a point that I dealt with very briefly; namely, the work that has been done on mechanisms of frost action in general. As Mr Figg says, the changes as a function of temperature in the state of adsorbed water within pores are the basis of more than one person's theory. I have referred to the work of Litvan and to a recent paper by Setser where the desorption of water as a result of changing chemical potential as a function of temperature due to the effect that Mr Figg mentions is considered.

As to the form of these particles, there is another theory of frost damage which may be relevant. Powers, having abandoned his hydraulic pressure mechanism, then proposed that the source of the expansion was in fact osmotic pressure caused by movement of water - unfrozen water - towards the concentrated layer of solution rejected ahead of ice bodies. He, therefore, would see the function of air entrainment as being due to water being drawn into the air voids where there is this concentrated solution layer, which is the probable source of the particles we observed.

What causes the particles to have the peculiar form that they have is a

mystery at the moment.   I have never seen Portlandite produced in this
form in any other context in cement paste, and I gather that Professor
Diamond has not done so either.   I would think the most likely explanation
is that the abietate ions, or other ions derived from the wood resin are
associating themselves with the surface of the nuclei and modifying the
growth morphology.   It is not even totally unreasonable to suggest that
the particles could be calcium abietate and not calcium hydroxide, because
calcium abietate is insoluble.   The only evidence against their being
calcium abietate is that one would have expected most of the air entraining
agent anyway to have been precipitated during the first day, and there was
also some slight evidence for 120° degree angles that would fit with the
sort of crystal structure that Portlandite has.

It is a very interesting comment, and one needs to do further work to come
up with some better ideas.

DR D DOUBLE (University of Oxford, UK):   Dr Page has observed a very
interesting effect in the increase in strength in samples that have been
subjected to freeze thawing.   The effect of calcium hydroxide may be
very relevant, but I want to suggest a possible alternative.   I wonder if
during the freeze/thawing cycle, the layers of hydration products around the
cement grains, which in effect, progressively retard the hydration reaction,
are not themselves disrupted.   What in fact is obtained is a higher degree
of hydration through easier access of water to the unhydrated cores during
the subsequent curing period.

DR C L PAGE: I think we would have to say that that is a reasonable
alternative explanation, and one could then account for the fact that this
is not observed in a plain non-air-entrained paste, presumably in terms of
there not being gross damage induced in the form of cracks put into the sample.
On the basis of the limited study that we performed, the only observations
that we could make which seemed to show up something unusual in the micro-
structure were the ones that I recorded.   I have indicated that it is a

tentative hypothesis that requires testing, and the alternative that Dr Double has just suggested would seem to be worth further investigation.

PROFESSOR S DIAMOND (Purdue University, USA):   Not a question but a comment, and a comment, perhaps, to preface the discussion which will almost certainly take place later.   At least in my opinion, a number of the most important details of the early hydration of Portland cement are still very controversial.   We have had a limited indication of the controversy between different people's ideas of what takes place in the first few hours of hydration.   We shall hear more of that, I am sure.   Until we can get straight and agree on what happens in ordinary hydration, it will be exceedingly difficult to get straight the secondary effect of any admixtures in modifying the process. The pitch I should like to make right now is that all of us keep an open mind when we hear explanations of how admixtures retard, accelerate or otherwise modify the early hydration reactions.   We do not really have these early hydration reactions pinned down adequately yet.   It is unfortunate, but I think that is a fair assessment of the current state.

CHAIRMAN: That is one hundred years on, as it were!

P POITEVIN (Spie-Batignolles, France):   I have a question on calcium chloride and the durability of plain concrete.   Some years ago I suggested using calcium chloride in the plain concrete of tetrapods in marine defence work, but there were objections, and I was told that the porosity of the concrete would be increased.   I understand from Professor Diamond's contribution that up to 28 days there is no combination of calcium chloride with the hydration products.   The calcium chloride will remain in a soluble state, and this situation is perhaps the cause of certain augmentation of the porosity, and the objection vis-a-vis the durability of such concrete.   I should like to know the Professor's opinion.

PROFESSOR DIAMOND: I am afraid I over-simplified.   The evidence is reasonably clear that much of the calcium chloride remains in the pore solution for quite a while; a week or two weeks perhaps.   I have no data beyond that.   Some of it, a relatively small proportion, 5 per cent, 10 per cent, or 15 per cent, finds its way into the hydration product. We pick up chloride in the CSH gel; not very much, but some. There are reports of occasional occurrences of Friedel's Salt in some pastes; not much, but some. I did not mean to imply that all of the calcium chloride remained in solution indefinitely; simply that most of it did. What I wanted to get across, and I may have glossed over the point, is that the pore solution <u>during the period in which the calcium chloride is having its accelerating effect</u> is still loaded with calcium chloride.

As to the influence of the calcium chloride on the porosity of the resultant concrete, there is considerable evidence suggesting that the pore size distribution of at least cement paste is changed; not necessarily the total porosity, but the size distribution, and there is a higher proportion of coarse pores. Presumably this leads to enhanced permeability, and perhaps to problems in durability in difficult environments where sulphate attack may take place. Details of this are still to some extent obscure.

J FIGG: I was struck in reading the preprints, as no doubt the two authors must have been, by the Hadley grains, the hollow shell structures with the depleted core. It seemed to fit very nicely between the two contributions, that this thickened membrane should have persisted in some way, perhaps to a later age. Certainly it had increased in thickness with time, and appears to be a proof of some sort of reaction at the rim and dissolution at the centre. I am not sure exactly how the two authors tie up, but it certainly seemed to be implied in Professor Diamond's contribution that when there was calcium chloride in the aqueous phase, there was an enhancement of the 'Hadley grain' effect.

One other comment. Professor Diamond mentioned that Friedel's Salt was only occasionally found. I understood that work at the VDZ laboratories in Dusseldorf had shown that with high C_3A cements, virtually all the chloride combined to form Friedel's Salt.

DR C L PAGE: From the point of view of effect on corrosion behaviour of embedded steel, there is very strong evidence that the C_3A content of the cement is closely related to the amount of chloride that can be tolerated before there is pitting breakdown of the oxide film on embedded steel.   We have got some results where we have measured the concentrations of calcium chloride which can be included in cement pastes of different C_3A contents before pitting takes place, and there is a strong correlation between C_3A content and the amount of added calcium chloride which produces any effect.   From the point of view of corrosion, there would appear to be quite clear evidence of binding of chloride by the aluminate phase.

CHAIRMAN: Is Dr Page saying the higher the C_3A, the less corrosive?

DR C L PAGE: Yes.   I am saying that by doing potentiodynamic scans — that is an electro-chemical technique — and by studying the electro-chemical behaviour of steel in pastes of different added chloride content, one can measure what is — approximately — the threshold level of chloride that has to be added to the paste in order to initiate pitting breakdown of the oxide film on the steel.   The amounts that will be tolerated are much higher in an ordinary Portland cement with, say, 12 per cent C_3A than in a sulphate-resisting Portland cement with maybe 3.5 per cent C_3A.

If one looks at the DTA (differential thermal analysis) curves in the two cases, for a 12 per cent C_3A ordinary Portland cement there is a fairly substantial endothermic peak at around 300° (signifying chloroaluminate), and in the case of the sulphate-resisting Portland cement with the much lower C_3A content this peak is almost negligible.

DR L MÜLLER (Heidelberger Zement AG, Germany FR):   The effect of an accelerator depends to a great degree on the water:cement ratio.   The same percentage of calcium formate can act as a retarder on a high water:cement ratio and as an accelerator at a low ratio.

Would Professor Diamond have any explanation of this phenomenon?

PROFESSOR S DIAMOND: With respect to that question, I am not acquainted
with the data, but it sounds as though it is a function of the actual concentrati
of formate ions in solution during the time of the dormancy - or induction period
if one perfers - and the breakout, when rapid hydration starts.   I suspect,
then, that the effect may very largely depend on the actual physical concentratio
of formate ions in the water that is present.   Obviously the high water:cement
ratio concentration would be proportionally, or roughly proportionally reduced.

I wanted to speak to the point raised by Mr Figg - who has a habit of raising
these critical points.   Yes.   Indeed there is a tempting parallelism that
might be drawn between the formation of rims around cement grains and the
subsequent dissolution of the cement inside the rim, called Hadley grains,
and seen in most cement paste hydration, and with calcium chloride treatment,
and the coating of gel-like material that Dr Double suggests forms in the very
early stages of hydration.   The question is, is this rim a successor to
the initial gelatinous coating?   It is tempting to suspect that it might be.
I have resisted the temptation very vigorously for a couple of reasons.
First, it is likely that one of the more likely reasons for a development
of the rim is the deposition of a layer of calcium hydroxide around the cement
grain somewhat similar to the deposition of a layer of calcium hydroxide around
other kinds of surfaces in contact with cement soup.   I have no direct evidence
of this, but I have been struck by the fact that there seems to be a
parellelism between duplex film and the early coating around PFA grains in PFA
cement, and the seeming parallelism of this to what one sees actually around
the cement grains.   Looking at a PFA cement in the early stages of hydration,
one has a great deal of difficulty distinguishing which grains are PFA and which
cement, except by the spherical shape of the PFA.   Perhaps something else
is going on in the early stages which to my view is different from Dr Double's
view of a CSH gelatinous layer that forms a membrane.

Another thing that causes me some difficulty is the presence of the space, at the
early stages during the dormant period, between the layer of gel membrane, and

the actual surface of the cement grain itself. Dr Double said that his drawing was not to scale and should not be so postulated, but very definitely the model depends on having different solutions, on two sides of a membrane. I think that the rim that we see which constitutes the outside of a Hadley grain forms in contact with a cement grain without leaving a gap, and that the gap forms only subsequently in the hydration period after active cement hydration has occurred. The two may have some relationship, but one cannot automatically suggest that the membrane grows into a Hadley shell around open space.

CHAIRMAN: If we go back to the model of the surface of the cement grain, at the moment of instantaneous contact with water - that can be imagined, a bit like water dissolving glass, as it were - there is a degree of combination and breakdown between the SiOCa etc., forming the lime and at the same time forming SI - OH groups, presumably silanol groups, which themselves dissociate, releasing protons and leaving the surface negatively charged. When Dr Double mentioned the recombination with calcium, was it the recombination of the dissociated silanol with calcium, leaving a residual positive charge rather than a negative charge? Does this picture of the instantaneous process that is going on tie in with such things as Zeta-potential measurements at the surface, where I believe the cement starts off as mildly positively charged? Is that a correct picture?

DR D DOUBLE: Basically I do not know. The problem is that one is talking about processes that are happening very close to the surface of the cement grain, and there is no easy way of finding out what is going on there. Certainly Zeta-potential measurements do indicate a positive charge at very early stages on the surface of hydrating C_3S grains. The way I drew it I was implying that the surface positive charge came about by the chemisorption of basic calcium ions on to the surface of the C_3S grain which would leave a residual positive charge.

DEVELOPMENTS

P BARTOS (Paisley College of Technology, UK):   I refer to the test methods described in the paper by Mr Edmeades and Dr Hewlett.   I shall illustrate two of the methods in more detail, and then I shall describe an alternative test method which is currently being developed.

First, a look at a well-known test.   Many people have worked with the DIN flow table which these days is the most commonly used test for the assessment of flowing, i.e., very high workability concretes.   What are its advantages in brie It is a very simple test which provides direct results.   One needs only to measure the spread, average two readings, and that is all.   It has, however, some practical limitations and problems, and what is more significant, this test cannot be incorporated into a general rheological system for assessing the workability of concrete.   It is difficult to find or to measure any rheological characteristics or derive them from the flow-table test results.

Mr Edmeades mentioned the two-point test machine several times in his paper. In Britain it is fairly well known, although there are probably no more than fifteen or twenty working two-point test machines available at the moment. For the benefit of those from overseas who have not yet come across this device, I shall briefly describe how it works.   It consists of a cylindrical container which is filled with fresh concrete.   A shaft with an impeller is lowered into the container, or the container is raised up so that the impeller is submerged in the concrete.   Then a speed for the rotation of the impeller is pre-set. This is the main variable in the test which will determine the shear rate of the concrete in the container.   The whole set-up is then started and the result is recorded as a pressure measured on a pressure gauge;   the pressure is required to power the hydraulic drive and the gearbox and cause the impeller to shear the concrete in the container.

To summarize;   what one has is an apparatus of about 1.5 m in height and the same length, powered by electricity.   The device has to be calibrated and a special calibration material should be used.   Only then will one get the

Orifice rheometer

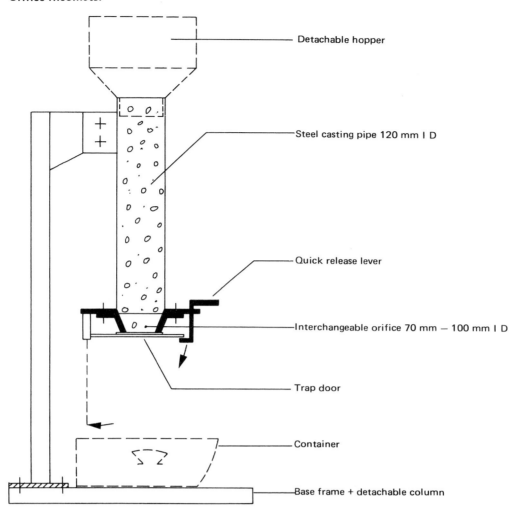

Detachable hopper

Steel casting pipe 120 mm I D

Quick release lever

Interchangeable orifice 70 mm – 100 mm I D

Trap door

Container

Base frame + detachable column

g and h factors which were quoted in the paper, either by calculation or by plotting pressure versus the rotor speed. This is the great advantage of the test. Unlike most other workability tests, it provides a much more accurate characterization of a concrete mix.

What are its disadvantages? The machine costs approximately £1,500, and it is a large and complex device. It is obviously very good for laboratory and research work but it is not really suitable for quick, on-site, tests to check whether concrete, which is about to be cast, is sufficiently fluid.

Let us, therefore, look at another test which is currently being developed. It is an orifice rheometer which in principle consists of a steel casting pipe, which is filled with a flowing fresh concrete mix. The casting pipe has

an interchangeable orifice, i.e., orifices of different diameters can be
attached to the bottom of the pipe.   This is necessary to prevent a 'plug'
flow of the contents out of the casting pipe.   For the test, one will take the
apparatus, a stopwatch, and a suitable container for collection of the concrete,
fill the casting pipe, and then release the trapdoor and measure the time it
will take for the concrete to flow out.   Clearly, the stiffer the concrete
mix, the slower the flow time.   If the concrete were too stiff, it would
probably remain in the casting pipe and not flow out at all.

Finally, let us explain what the development aims to do and the uses of this test.

We have already begun a programme of site trials to see that the values obtained
from the test have some meaning to the engineer and the concrete technologist
on site.   This, incidentally, is still a problem with the factors from the
two-point test because so far it can only be related, with difficulty, to slump
or other less satisfactory test methods.   There is no bulk of data from
site trials yet available.   Here I wish to acknowledge all the support we
are getting from the Readymix Company, the concrete industry, and in particular
Trumix Limited.

The second is about the theoretical basis.   Is it a single-point test, or
is it just a completely empirical test?   When we fill the whole casting pipe
with concrete, at the instant that the trap door is opened shear stresses will
develop at the narrowed part in the orifice area due to the pressure of the
column of the concrete.   But the shear rate at this instant will be zero.
When the concrete starts to flow out, shear rate will increase, and at the
same time the shear stress will decrease as the column of the concrete becomes
smaller.   Obviously it is a test in which the shear stress and the shear rate
vary.   It requires a complex mathematical analysis to provide a correct
model, but although it may be a little more difficult than for the two-point
test, it is certainly not impossible.   Work is in progress to establish a
mathematical model and to fit the orifice rheometer into a general system
for measuring workability of fresh flowing concrete.

Finally, <u>the test is intended to be a site test, and simplicity is considered essential</u>.   I personally do not like the stopwatch.   It should be quite possible to develop the test into a 'go/no-go' device, which, with a suitable orifice, could be used to check whether the concrete is sufficiently fluid without measuring the flow-time.   Obviously, for the construction site, the simpler the better.

DR D BERRY (BP Chemicals Limited, UK):   Let me first stress that I am a chemist and not a materials scientist.   Nevertheless, I should like to congratulate the contributors on excellent presentations from which I have learnt a great deal.

Following on from Mr Rixom's paper on new developments, I had intended, having read the preprints, to react to the statement about the lack of development of chloride-free accelerators.   However, he has now touched on three developments. He mentioned a British company that has developed a complex formate salt. I thought I would enlarge upon this.   Just to sketch out the development. Over the last two-and-a-half years, BP Chemicals have developed a new chemical species which is a complex salt of sodium formate and formic acid, and it can form the basis of a new chloride-free accelerator package.   A few words about the chemical itself.   In this product, formic acid is complexed with sodium formate to give a high-strength solution (68 per cent) of salt in water. This is one advantage, compared to calcium formate, where we are talking about 14 per cent strength solutions.   Because the formic acid is complexed, the solution compared to formic acid itself has certain advantages.   For example, it is less volatile and safer to handle, but the formic acid is still available for chemical reaction.   I shall come to that point later, if I am to be allowed a few words on my theory for the mechanism of the reaction of this material.

Certain tests have been done with the complex sodium formate salt comparing it with calcium formate, and what we found is that compared to setting times and early strength development, the material is more effective than calcium formate.

For example, 1 per cent active ingredient of our formate salt is equivalent to 1.5 per cent calcium formate on early strength development, and 0.5 per cent of the formate salt is comparable to 1.0 per cent calcium formate on setting time. That is a rough picture.   We have also done corrosion tests including both the types mentioned by Mr Rixom.   Polarisation curves indicate that the complex salt with mild steel test pieces simply exhibits the normal transpassive/ passive corrosion behaviour on the surface.   These were done using a calcium hydroxide saturated solution as a simulation of the conditions inside the concrete pores.   We have also embedded mild steel rods in mortar similar to those described in the slides that were shown earlier, where by visual examination - not fancy television cameras picking out pits, the complexed formate salt gives test pieces with the same appearance as the control.

A few words about the mechanism.   My feeling for the mechanism is this. The formic acid is free to react.   I feel that because it is completely miscible in water, we have a system where the formic acid gets to the actual hydration sites and reacts with the free calcium hydroxide to form calcium formate in situ, so that calcium formate and sodium formate are formed at the site of hydration.

Dr Page mentioned calcium hydroxide crystals.   What struck me was that maybe the mechanism could relate to the formic acid mopping up these free crystals.

DR S DIAMOND: The use of calcium nitrite as an accelerator and a corrosion inhibitor simultaneously has been in the literature for a good many years.   The question that has always been doubted was that at low concentrations there seemed to be a considerable question as to the effectiveness of the corrosion resistance characteristics of this material.   Rumour had it that the stuff acted as a corrosion promoter rather than a corrosion inhibitor.   As a result of large-scale testing, a reputable company has now decided to market this material, and I am wondering if Mr Rixom would care to comment on how they handle this particular problem.

M R RIXOM (Cormix Division, Joseph Crosfield & Sons Ltd., UK):
This should be very easy, because I do not know.   It is interesting that
all of the results I have seen - and there are quite a lot of them apart from the
simple list of results that I put up - all start at 2.0 per cent.   I think that
is so of all the work that was presented in March 1980 at World of Concrete.
That is quite unusual.   When we normally talk about accelerating materials,
we study it at 0.5 per cent, 1.0 per cent, and so forth.   It is an interesting
question, and it was also raised by L H McCurrich in a previous discussion
regarding the value of such a material in a concrete which is porous or cracked,
in that it seemed unlikely that it could protect the steel when it was exposed,
and therefore one could get corrosion attack there.   The point I made was that
it would offer an interesting chloride-free accelerator.   I am not suggesting
that I have enough information to say so, but on its platform as a corrosion
inhibitor there may be many questions like the one that Professor Diamond posed,
but as a chloride-free accelerator it has some merit.

DR L MÜLLER: I saw from Mr Edmeades's paper that the cement used had a very
low alkaline oxide content.   In German conditions we would call such a cement
an "NA" cement for use for alkaline-sensitive aggregates.   Has the combination
of superplasticiser and retarder ever been tested with cements with a higher
potassium oxide content, because then there is a danger of syngenite $(CaSO_4.K_2SO_4.H_2O)$
formation and quicker stiffening than there is without any retarder?

R M EDMEADES (Cementation Research Limited, UK):   The cement we use we would
regard as being a fairly typical Portland cement in the UK.   There are very few
that contain more than 1.5 per cent total alkalies, and so I must confess that we
have not tried out our admixture combination with a high-alkali cement. Perhaps
we should do so in the future.

B D BLACK (BP Chemicals Ltd., UK):   If sodium nitrite is added to
cement in an admixture formulation, does that not then give the constituents
of calcium nitrite anyway, and why does sodium nitrite then not give the
same effect?

Secondly, would Mr Rixom comment on any evidence that is available from experience of using calcium formate in the field, on its corrosivity.

CHAIRMAN: The point that Mr Rixom made was that the total level of sodium residing in the concrete by the addition of a sodium salt is what was problematic. There is no doubt that it may well be the calcium salt _in situ_ but one is still adding sodium by virtue of adding the sodium salt to begin with.
I wanted to ask what is the relative additional level of the added sodium in the sense of adding to the sodium that is there already in relation to the alkali aggregate problem.   In quantitative terms, is it a meaningful increase?

MR M R RIXOM: Unless I misunderstood the question, there are three questions there.   If I could take them in order, I was asked what is unique about calcium nitrite when the sodium nitrite is being used and is acceptable so that it is put in, one will end up with calcium nitrite anyway.   I have asked myself many times with other things, like sodium chloride and calcium chloride, and stannous chloride which I have seen in another paper.   There are several materials where one would assume that a very rapid interchange would occur on addition to the concrete, and yet they do behave very differently in their effectiveness, and sodium chloride for calcium chloride is a good example.   There is no doubt about the effectiveness of calcium nitrite in comparison to sodium nitrite – the difference is a real one, but I cannot understand why.

The second question asked whether I had personally ever come across any problem, or any instance suggesting that calcium formate has caused corrosion in a concrete situation.   The answer is emphatically no, I have not.

The third question asks how much sodium it actually adds.   From the figures they were adding sodium nitrite, 2 to 3 per cent by weight of cement of the solution of material, which itself is 30 per cent, so that is 1.0 per cent by solids, of which probably one third is sodium.   We are talking about certainly less than 0.3 per cent by weight of cement.   A small amount. Whether the mechanism is solely the addition of sodium ion, or some other chemical effect to which the sodium nitrite contributes in the alkali expansion system I do not know.

DR N TENOUTASSE: I should like to provide some further information about the action of calcium formate.   Mr Rixom called both calcium chloride and calcium formate accelerators, but we have observed that although calcium formate is an accelerator for the hydration of C_3A it has no action in the hydration of C_3S.   Calcium chloride accelerates the hydration of C_3S.   The reason is that calcium formate is generally an accelerator at setting time, and calcium chloride is an accelerator in the hardening of cement.

At Brussels University we have made a mixture of calcium chloride and calcium formate, and we have observed, using a mixture of 0.5 of calcium chloride, and about 1.5 calcium formate, in calorimeter tests, the same accelerator effect as with about 3 per cent calcium chloride.   But, we have not done any strength tests.

I have some information about another salt used as an accelerator - sodium aluminate.   It is a good accelerator, especially for Portland cement and cement with fly ash.   In cements containing fly ash, we have no problem with aggregate-alkali reaction, because fly ash is a good pozzolana for avoiding any reaction between alkali and aggregate.

CHAIRMAN: I imagine that every admixture manufacturer has made note of that particular chemical!

M R RIXOM: With acceleration, particularly of chloride-free material, I am very reluctant to be emphatic about anything.   But I must take issue with the suggestion that calcium formate is in no way an accelerator of the C_3S phase. Work has been carried out with the microcalorimeter at the C & CA in the UK which does indicate that it does have an accelerating effect on the C_3S phase, although I will grant there was an alteration in the shape of the C_3A phase curve which did lead us to believe that there was a difference between calcium formate and calcium chloride.   But it is still relevant that calcium formate does accelerate the C_3S phase.

Dr Tenoutasse then went on to talk about sodium aluminate. This material is quite widely used as an accelerator, but for shotcreting and sprayed concrete applications. Our normal experience – just as a warning to people because it is a useful material – in normal concrete, whilst giving a very quick-setting concrete mix, it normally will affect adversely the long term strength of the concrete.

P POITEVIN (Spie-Batignolles, France):   I should like to comment on air entrainment; not from the point of view of its effect on the freeze/thaw resistance, but on the other effects which were alluded to.   Mr McCurrich showed a quay in Arabia with huge concrete blocks and said that the durability of those blocks had been improved by air entrainment.   Dr Page has already said that among the other effects of air entrainment on hardened concrete, impermeability and durability were somewhat improved.   I am not sure of this improvement.   I consider that the improvement is due to the improvement in fresh concrete, like no bleeding, and this kind of improvement is reflected in hardened concrete, but it can be obtained by other methods.

Lastly, for several years, systematic testing has been carried out in Paris, in the Laboratoire Centrale des Ponts et Chaussees, on air entrained concrete. In France, air entrained concrete is used only for concrete road slabs.   From micrographs, it was evidenced that around air bubbles there were fine cracks, but none too fine, so that the possibility in concrete immersed in water to suffer from water penetration was not excluded.   This is not to deny the beneficial effects of air entrainment on freeze/thaw resistance, but as to the impermeability of concrete, these systematic tests show that the improvement is dubious.   Many consultants are still specifying entrainment for marine work or for hydraulic works to improve impermeability, and I would be interested in learning of any systematic experiments that demonstrate these effects.

L H McCURRICH (Fosroc Construction Chemicals Ltd., UK): That is fair comment.   Basically, air entrainment has gained its reputation

for improving durability by reducing permeability on the theory that the voids
break up the capillaries.   I have certainly seen theoretical explanations
as to why it reduces permeability, because of the surface tension effect where
the capillary goes into the void, and therefore the voids do not fill with water.
This also explains why the voids in air entrained concrete do not fill with
water.   That, to my mind, has been the reason, and possibly a satisfactory
explanation as to why air entrained concrete has lower permeability.   I am
interested in the comments made by Msr Poitevin, and in knowing whether anybody
can quote quantitative permeability measurement data.   I have seen data to
support that in the past, but I cannot quote the reference offhand.

CHAIRMAN: If I might add a comment.   I think the permeability to which
Mr McCurrich is referring would be the permeability at very low-pressure
gradients;   in other words, it would be permeability in relation to absorbtive
capacity rather than Darcy type flow permeability.   At high pressures, whether
small voids or large voids are put in, if it is interconnected voidage, then it
will pass water.   It is a question, really, of getting a better apparent
permeability response at low-pressure gradients.

R L MUNN (BMI Limited, Australia):   I had some comment about Dr Levitt's
paper.   I found it very interesting.   Oddly enough, we seem to have drawn
the same conclusions he has about using other admixtures in combination with
pigments, or at least very similar conclusions, but there is one important
difference.   Dr Levitt spoke specifically of waterproofers, as being a term
that is commonly used, although I believe it is the wrong term to use for that.
More particularly, the stearate type of admixtures in combination with the use
of colour pigments as being an improvement.

In Australia, we fairly widely use pozzolanas in the concrete.   In fact,
normal concrete will have quite considerable proportions of pozzolanas used as
partial cement replacements.   We have discovered that these have a significant
beneficial effect on the colour retention in the concrete mixes when pigments
are also included.   I believe I have finally found the explanation for that –

227

Dr Levitt has kindly given it. Obviously what was happening was that we were tying up some of the efflorescence in the lime which normally appears. I can also bear that out that in general construction work, since we have been using these pozzolanas in such a way, the degree of efflorescence on exposed surfaces has dramatically reduced. I believe this is probably to do with this particular effect.

I also feel that the same sort of thing could probably be said in general terms in what we describe as permeability reducing admixtures. We have a strange standard which covers these products. It would cover all sorts of things, including polyethylene oxides, limestone fines, and other mineral admixtures - all sorts of things that will change the permeability structure of the concrete. All of these will have some effect on the lasting colour of concrete, but probably the best of the lot is a fly ash, or a ground granulated slag, because it also acts in a chemical way as well as having the physical effect of reducing permeability.

DR M LEVITT: I have to thank Mr Munn for that contribution. It is something we have also found out - that there are certain drawbacks with the addition of these fine materials which either eat up the free lime or act as void filling and therefore impermeability promotive agents. The only times we have been able to use things like fly ash in coloured concrete is when we are dealing with dark colours of concrete, such as the reds, the browns and the dark yellows. The trouble with fly ash is that once one starts to add it to the lighter colours, one will tend to lose a lot. Once we were pigmenting a concrete a yellow colour, and a yellow colour pigment is the devil to use in any case, and we had about 25 per cent cement replacement with fly ash, and the fly ash had a slightly blue colour to it, and the concrete came out green. It was not quite what we wanted, but the architect, luckily, did change his specification!

In all due seriousness, I would point out that these materials certainly do improve impermeability, and I would support Mr Munn fully, but I would still

228

state that we want something that is even better if we can get it. The water repellents are really the answer when these other materials are not available. Bearing in mind that the demand of water by fly ash is not very much, if any limestone dust is added to a concrete mix, the water content has to be increased to maintain the workability, and this is not always the answer unless there are very small quantities of limestone dust there.

CHAIRMAN: Just to put a slightly more quantitative interpretation on that comment, it has been estimated that the reduction in permeability, or more properly the reduction in flow, water flow, in a porous material such as concrete is proportional to the change in surface area to the power 2. If one were to take a cement with a nominal specific surface area of 3,000 sq cms/gm and to add to that a mineral, just for the sake of argument, a fine bentonite clay with a specific surface area of about 100,000 sq cms/gm, some 1 or 2 per cent addition of such a fine mineral changes the internal surface area by a factor of about 3, which means an internal water reduction flow rate of a factor of 9, so very small percentage additions can make a substantial reduction in the permeability or water passage capability of the porous material.

SUMMING UP

DR P C HEWLETT — Chairman (Cementation Research Ltd., UK):
I shall endeavour to sum up today's proceedings, and I must be forgiven if, as a consequence of the contributions, my comments are somewhat generalized.

We have been treated to eight papers of both excellence and relevance from persons committed on the one hand academically and on the other commercially to probing and demanding answers at a fundamental level, and an applied level, in the areas of cement hydration and admixture function. It is perhaps significant that the Admixtures Congress should start in this way. If we are still asking questions about cement, it is surely not strange that questions are being asked about admixtures. However, there is a balance between total understanding and practical exploitation and innovation that has to be struck. The functions, both of cement and admixtures, are obviously intimately dependent one upon the other. It is from this base that admixtures are projected and not as a thing apart, depending on intrigue and secrecy.

I mentioned earlier that the two sessions were aimed at adding to the technical credibility of admixtures. I think that objective was well met today, and I trust has given some perspective on the groundwork surrounding the use of current admixtures and their ongoing development. For specific recognition I would mention that be it admixtures, admixture and cement or cement alone, we do not know all there is to know. Engineers, researchers and developers should be prepared to pose new models, accept responsible change and not be too dogmatic. Perhaps we shall never know all the answers. The same receptive attitude of mind could usefully extend to specifiers, consulting engineers and local authorities, and indeed the entire construction industry, which is not, by and large, noted for its materials innovation. Acknowledgement of useful materials development focussed on home and overseas needs. Behind the somewhat pedestrian use of concrete, there is obviously an area of continuous change and data gathering. Such a thought, I would suggest, is reassuring.

The move from natural to synthetic materials may have come as a surprise to some delegates; that goats' milk, pigs' fat, blood and beef tallow have been replaced by chemically tailored molecules having a predetermined and reproducible performance. Indeed the identity of compositions have been honestly disclosed. By today's contributors admixture formulators have to some degree declared the benefits and limitations of some of their materials in a co-operative and objective manner. This style of working, closely integrated with the cement, concrete and construction industry should be positively encouraged.

To quote the opening words of the President of the Concrete Society:
"Bringing science and engineering closer together".   I think the papers
presented today, is the sort of thing he had in mind.

Usage is based on understanding rather than a cataloguing of macrophenomena;
benefits that can accrue as a result of controlling what happens at the micro
level.

On a cautionary note.   Clearly the need for a trouble-free accelerator
should not be satisfied by materials that may have a corrosion legacy of their
own.   It is also reassuring to observe that admixture developers are
conscious of the need to be sensitive about this problem area.   Indeed,
it is they that are raising the matter, and that is to the good.

SPECIFICATIONS AND CONTROL

L H McCURRICH (Fosroc Construction Chemicals, UK):   Two points in connection
with Mr Tipler's paper on reviewing performance standards for admixtures.
Two particular traps into which people fall - and I would particularly address
these remarks to those who are concerned with drawing up performance standards
for admixtures.

The first of these is the question of tolerances.   In most of these
standards, one has to have a tolerance on the slump or the compacting factor of
the test mix that has to be plus or minus some value of the mean value for the
reference mix.   These tolerances can lead one into no end of problems.
This is something that many people in the industry are experiencing, in that,
for example, taking the test mix versus a reference mix, if the tolerance on the
compacting factor is working in favour of the admixture, a very poor quality
admixture will pass the requirements of strength subsequently, or if the compacting
factor tolerance works against it, even a first-rate admixture may have difficulty
in meeting the subsequent strength requirement, because not enough water will
have been reduced in the first instance.   In the UK there is a very interesting

move proposed now by the B R E to amend the standard to take out this problem of tolerances, but it is still a problem worldwide.

The second problem, which is also a bit confusing in Mr Tipler's paper, is the definition of initial and final setting times.   For example, there are different classifications in the US and the UK standards.   In the UK standard, the definition of the final stiffening time is the same as the initial setting time in the USA standards.   We find, using standards worldwide, this difference in defining setting times leads to no end of confusion.

T J TIPLER   (Cement & Concrete Association, UK):
I should like to thank Mr McCurrich for making those two points. There is no need for me to make any comment on the first but on the second I should like to do so.   In the comparative tables at the end of the paper there are quite a number of footnotes which I used to try to eliminate any ambiguities which might arise from the fact that methods of test differ from one country to another.   Evidently I have not entirely succeeded in this and I should perhaps amend the text of the paper before it is published in the discussion volume of the Proceedings.

J FIGG (Harry Stanger Ltd., UK):
A point that was brought out very well by Mr Connolly - although its importance may have been missed - in connection with his first case study. It illustrates how very important it is to ask the right questions.   When an engineer, or other person, is in contact with a chemist and is asking that something be done with a sample of concrete he must consider what sort of help he really wants.   If he only wants to find out whether the right amount of admixture is present, the answer could have been 'yes', and yet clearly the concrete was no good.   He should have asked why it had not performed properly.   It is very important that this discussion or dialogue between the people involved shall be undertaken.   It is no easy matter to unravel concrete chemically and to find out what reactions have occurred, and it certainly does not help if the communications are not good at the start.

P POITEVIN (Spie-Batignolles, France):

Mr Tipler is to be congratulated for his excellent presentation of a very
important and difficult subject.   In particular, he has understood French
regulations perfectly.   They are difficult to understand because they are in
documents that are not widely known.   Those regulations which were issued by
COPLA, a Ministry organisation, are to be replaced by the Standards
Organisation of France, called 'AFNOR'.   All the members of the AFNOR
working party will be pleased to learn from Mr Tipler's paper that the
synthesis of the world standards on admixtures find some complement in the
actual French Regulations.   The standard mixes in concrete are a very useful
tool for the clients, because they provide a means of comparing the performance
of several trade marks.   It is important to note that the two cements used not
only have a fixed C_3A content, but that they come from fixed mills and they
are always the same.   It is truly a reference list.   All products are tested
with the same cements; two cements only.

Secondly, a remark about calcium chloride.   In France calcium chloride is not
considered to be an admixture, because it is a chemical product and not a
proprietary product.   I think that that will be altered in the new standard
because, logically, it is a chemical admixture.   The reference did not
include a regulation on the use of chloride and calcium chloride.   But it is
published in the form of a DTU - an official regulation for use - and it has
been recently updated and is quite liberal.

Lastly, a general question.   In the chemical content of admixtures, some
part of this chemical content must be required by a standard, because some
chemicals - e.g., calcium chloride or sulphur - are necessary to permit the use
in a particular country.   But, is not the main chemical component of an
admixture quoted for each product?   In France, it is considered as
proprietary.   It is not quoted in the <u>fiche d'agrèment</u>.   Proprietary
products must not be compelled to have their whole chemical content divulgated
but the main components must be stated.   If there is an international
standard, it should be a requirement.

CHAIRMAN: I am sure the answer to that question is 'yes'.

T J TIPLER: I would make the point that the standards very often ask for the main generic type of material giving the main action to be stated.   That is a very common requirement.

R L MUNN (B M I Ltd., Australia):   I found Mr Tipler's paper very interesting.   Considering that it is such a massive task to review so many standards, I could quite understand if there were a few little 'loose ends' left over.   I wanted to clarify one or two of those.

First, I noticed the paper compares the current Australian standards very favourably with the RILEM recommendations, but I should point out that the Australian standard pre-dates those recommendations by some years.   I do not know whether the dog wags the tail or the other way round.   In comment, I should say that there is an Australian standard in existence for permeability reducing admixtures, which was omitted there.   It appears as a Miscellaneous Publication of the Standards Association, but as no Australian standards are compulsory until they are adopted by a specification, there is nothing to stop a specifier adopting a miscellaneous publication as part of his standard. So the rules do exist there for it.

There is also one for colouring pigments which covers the colouring materials that we discussed in an earlier session.   This is quite a separate standard and appears under the control of the Cement and Pozzolana Committee of the Standards - a place where perhaps one would not expect to find it.   But it is there, and does exist.

One could get the impression that it was possible to get quite irresponsible about chloride levels in admixtures if there were not some controls on this. What is required in Australia is that a manufacturer declares the maximum level of chloride inclusion in his admixture so that it is possible then for the specifier, and for the user of concrete who intends to use such a material to determine whether that level of chloride would be consistent with the end use of the concrete for which it is proposed. The system works quite well, and I would commend it. I am not a firm believer in blanket bans on materials such as chloride because there are uses for which they are entirely appropriate. One I would commend is in a situation where there are no reinforcing steels in the concrete.

I feel that there are horses for courses and these things need to be examined. There is a series of retarders in common use which do not contain chlorides, and which we have found to be very effective under the Australian climatic conditions; sometimes temperatures approaching the $38^{\circ}C$ figures that we heard might appear in the Middle East.

One comment on Mr Connolly's paper. We do quite a bit of admixture analysis and examination along the lines that he proposes, in Australia, but we found it almost impossible to analyse adequately to find admixtures given a completely unknown set of raw materials. It is virtually impossible to tell somebody to go and find out what was in that. If one knows the raw materials and one knows what was likely to have been there, then it is possible to get quite reasonable quantitative estimates of the proportions of admixtures and doses that were used in that concrete, provided that one can get a reasonable sample of it.

CHAIRMAN: As a Readymix Concrete producer, I know that Ready Mixed Concrete first started in Australia. Now I know that admixtures first started there!

J D CONNOLLY (Erlin, Hime Associates, Inc., USA): I think Mr Munn has made a good point. I do not know whether they use infra-red spectrophotometric methods with this type of extraction procedure in Australia, but we can, for example, be quite certain as to the presence of particular admixture components in concrete. We analyse for chemicals, and we can say whether a product component, named X, is present. We can determine if these components are present, but at some stage the presence and relative amounts of the different components detected has to be translated into some proprietary or trade name admixture.   One can go so far, and at that point there has to be some feedback from the job situation.   This is an important part of any analytical work; or any problem solving as far as that goes.   This was illustrated by Mr Figg.   When a project is started, the analysts should be given the directions to find out what the cause of the problem was, using what techniques they feel are necessary.   Part of the dialogue that follows is the presentation of the analyst's data back to those asking the questions, in an effort to interpret it as fully as possible.   Supplying as much information as possible at the time the sample is submitted, and then interchanging all the data back and forth both ways is a key part of this whole analytical procedure and problem-solving technique.

DR P C HEWLETT (Cementation Research Ltd., UK):   I should like to take up some points made by Mr Tipler and perhaps expand on one of the underlying difficulties of compliance/performance testing.

British Standard 5075 Part 1 establishes admixture performance against a reference cement.   The reference cement that is chosen is usually complying with its own standard, in that case British Standard 12.   However, cements from different sources, while still conforming with the appropriate standard, have large variations.   So much so, that an admixture may comply with the standard for cement, let us say from source A, but not comply when tested against a cement from source B.   This is something of a real dilemma, since compliance testing against each individual cement used, say, for a particularly large contract, cannot be justified on the basis of cost or time.

Expanding the admixture standard compliance limits may well dilute the purpose of the standard and embrace admixtures that would normally not comply. I would suggest the purpose of the standard is to establish conformity of performance in order to reassure the user, on an occasional basis.   This being the case, are we satisfied that there is sufficient standardization of the cements to make admixture compliance meaningful?

T J TIPLER: That is a big question.   I can only agree that, if -
as is the case in the UK - there are available a considerable number of
ordinary Portland cements, which come from different sources and which vary
in their composition, then an admixture, which performs adequately when
tested with one of these, may not do so when used with another rather
different ordinary Portland cement.   I do not think that the comments I have
made in the paper are in any sense a criticism of the admixture, but rather
an attempt to underline the fact that there is something of a problem here.
I agree that what we are seeking to do, or what is being attempted, is to
provide in these standards a systematic procedure for checking conformity,
quality and reliability.

In the UK, the Cement Admixtures Association has discussed with the cement
companies the provision of a "typical" ordinary Portland cement.   The
term "typical" itself gives rise to difficulties.   I understand that in
certain other countries, admixture manufacturers supply slightly different
formulations in different areas to suit the cements which are locally
available.   In a continental country where much greater distances are
involved, that is probably a very reasonable way of tackling the problem.
But in the UK., where the distances are so much smaller, and where on a
large job different cements might be used having different compositions,
that solution is unlikely to be practical.

I realise that I have talked around the problem and not directly answered
the question!

CHAIRMAN: I am sure that the audience expected some questions not to be
answered, and for some things to be left to the future.

CASE HISTORIES

DR M LEVITT (John Laing R & D Limited, UK):   The table that Mr George
put up on the slide was very interesting.   I do not dispute any of the

figures, but the Total Costs row, where the figures varied from about DM 21 per cu m down to about DM 3 per cu m was preceded by the entitlement 'Total Cost'. I believe these are total labour costs and exclude materials.

Mr George made one comment when he showed a slide of some precast concrete piles that went to a contract in Iran - and in his summary these were transferred to Saudi Arabia.   I am not particularly interested in which country they went to, but he did make the comment that the higher strength obtained with the superplasticisers improved the impact or shock resistance. It has always been my understanding that the elasticity of concrete improves the lower the strength.   I would be grateful if Mr George would comment.

W H GEORGE (Hoechst UK Limited, UK):   On Dr Levitt's first point, I mentioned that the figures at the bottom of the slide did exclude material costs when I showed the slide.   The actual amount for materials - the two righthand columns - materials cost, ie., admixture cost, would have been somewhere around DM 6 per cu m.   In fact, in the middle column, overall costs would have been somewhere about DM 14.40.   Nevertheless, there is still a saving of DM 6 per cu m, which is certainly not insignificant. With the other one there would have been a slightly smaller saving.   Even taking into account the cost of the admixture, those figures still show a considerable saving.

On Dr Levitt's other question, about the precast piles for Iran - and not Saudi Arabia as I said in the summary - the contractor looked at the piles initially for high strength, and then I believe I modified that later to say that he used a superplasticiser eventually to save water and save cement, and it was in this way, i.e., by reducing the cement content of the mix, that he improved the impact resistance of the piles, and not by increasing the strength of the piles.   If Dr Levitt misunderstood me, then I apologise, but I did stress that they saved cement by saving water, and that improved the impact resistance.   I also mentioned at the time that the cost of the admixture was more than paid for by the savings in cement.

DR C D JOHNSTON (University of Calgary, Canada):   Mr George said a
great deal about flowing concrete.   Was any of it air entrained flowing
concrete, and if it was, has he any special recommendations as to how to get
a satisfactory entrained air void system in flowing concrete?

W H GEORGE: The first example we gave in the paper was from a large
American housebuilder (Fox and Jacobs).   It is standard practice in America
to use air entrainment so that that job would certainly have been air
entrained concrete.   Our experience in the UK on the use of superplasticisers
in air entrained concrete - my particular experience was on the Ninian Central
Platform - superplasticisers were used in the construction of the units in
the splash zone for that platform, and the client insisted that that was air
entrained concrete for durability, and that a superplasticiser was still
needed for placement.   The tests that we did showed that with a
superplasticiser, the air content of the mix was reduced.   This was
compensated for by increasing the dosage of the air entrainer.   My own personal
view is that that was probably not necessary, because what the superplasticiser
was doing was to release the entrapped air, so that the entrained air
content was probably still the same.   But nevertheless, it can be done
and it can be done successfully.

I believe that one small road job has been done in the UK where they have
had no problem with air entrained superplasticised concrete, and there are
quite a number of road jobs in Germany and an experimental road job in
Denmark where they have successfully used air entrained flowing concrete.

P POITEVIN (Spie-Batignolles, France):   Recently we had occasion to
test flowing concrete in a nuclear power plant concreting operation.   It was
the slab of a containment structure.

The first problem with flowing concrete comes with the specifiers.   They
fear high slumps and they stop us at about 10 cm.   We can use flowing
concrete, but not to its fullest advantage with this limitation.

Secondly, in the table which was projected, there were three columns. It must have carried a fourth column; ordinary pumped concrete with a normal water-reducing admixture. It was sufficient to pump the concrete and we certainly needed more manpower, but the economics for us lay in the fact that with ordinary water-reducing admixtures, its price was a third of the other admixture - the superplasticiser. The savings in manpower with pumped concrete against bucket concrete amount to perhaps ten or twenty per cent, so we use pumped concrete. But with a limited slump of 10 cms there, we, as contractors, cannot use flowing concrete to its full economic advantage.

R KIESLER (Hoechst UK Limited, UK):

I appreciate what Msr Poitevin says about his experiences. One should distinguish the true differences when superplasticisers are used. A superplasticiser is used to improve productivity on the one hand, or to change the properties of the concrete, on the other. It is very difficult, I agree, to work out where the advantage lies, but when concrete with a higher workability is pumped, then, for example, the time, the man hours, will be brought down. We have tested this in Europe in the past.

I was very much involved in the US in a testing series for nuclear projects. Following the trouble at Harrisburg, everyone was suddenly afraid to use concrete, and I think it is now proved that concrete is an excellent material to protect the population from any danger. Harrisburg has proved that too. We know from the nuclear projects how difficult it is to vibrate the concrete to avoid these holes in the concrete. Many tests have been carried out over the years, I believe over three years, which have proved that the superplasticised concrete has given them the safety they needed to be sure that troubles will not arise.

CHAIRMAN: The impression I have gained so far from today's session is that there are certain purposes for which admixtures must be used. It could well be that we have reached a stage where the admixture suppliers do not have to sell their admixtures as such but should work together with the producer to ascertain which admixtures can be most useful in particular applications.   The other impression I have is that suppliers can play a big part in defining what we mean by savings.   There must be a proper examination of this.   When it comes to site-placed concrete, the British ready mixed industry is still suffering from what we call the unit cost approach, i.e., of just looking only at one element, whereas the contractor should be looking at all elements of the cost of placing concrete on site. I think this came out of the presentations by Dr Taylor and Dr Sparrow. They looked at the whole production process and they have certain requirements of the properties of the concrete, they have certain requirements of productivity, as Mr Kiesler said.   By the admixture suppliers working together with contractors and makers of concrete, we can produce a finished product which is the right compromise between economy and fitness for purpose.

DR P C HEWLETT (Cementation Research Limited, UK):
The implication in the first part of the session was that perhaps there was some fundamental incompatibility between the principle of endeavouring to entrain stable air in concrete and at the same time impart very high workability using superplasticisers.   Coincidentally, but eighteen months later as it were, the same concern was expressed at the CANMET Conference. I should like to offer some sort of reasoning to allay some of the fears.

If we go back to Professor Kreijger's talk, he looked at the fundamental interaction of some of these chemical admixtures on the surface of the sand and of the large aggregate as well as of the cement, and a fairly coherent picture emerges.   We recall that all commonly available air entraining agents are all basically anionic surfactants.   That means that they impart their effect by residual negative charge.   We can picture that very much along the lines of Professor Kreijger's reasoning.   If the surfactant with the negative terminal end is added to the concrete, there will be stable air bubble formation, with some degree of attraction to the alternative charge on the surface of the cement, and ditto that on the aggregate.   As a consequence of that general form of mutual charge cancelling, some degree of coming together of the particles and air is achieved.   It is that coming together, or the formation of that aggregate - air - cement - air - aggregate bridge that shows itself as cohesion, or fattiness in an air entrained mix. At the same time, there will be a degree of enhanced workability as a result of the air bubbles acting as some form of internal lubricant.   The term 'ball bearings' was used (yesterday).   It is picturesque, but it is probably more complex than that.   Nevertheless, the overall effect is one of improved workability whilst maintaining cohesion.

If we go to superplasticisers, or plasticisers for that matter, because they are both members of the same family, then these too are anionic surfactants.   They are not different in principle, but they are different in fine structure and mechanism, and the difference depends very much upon the chemical functionality of this tail end of the surfactant molecule, which to all intents is sitting there doing nothing in the case of an air entrainer.   When we come to superplasticisers and plasticisers, it dominates. We have a situation that I think will be pictured something along these lines.   The backbone is now adsorbed.   The negative charge is exposed, both on the cement surface, the aggregate and the air bubble.   So much so, that one will get a complete reversal of the previous trend, and instead of getting cohesion one may get mutual repulsion, and it is that repulsive effect that gives rise to the dispersing, and hence the high-workability aspect.

That being the case, if both the superplasticiser or plasticiser and the air entrainer are used together, there will be some mix of both these separate effects, and it probably is right to infer, initially at least, that the effects on these materials are mutually competitive for both the air bubbles and the surfaces, and they are mutually excluding.

What is the overall effect, or how can we use this?   Can we get a degree

of compatibility?   I would suggest we can.   When I compiled <u>this</u>
overhead, I had no idea what Mr Moksnes would say, but he has confirmed what
is after all a fairly simple picture, and the problem to which Dr Sparrow
referred in the earlier part of the session.   But perhaps the way to go
about trying to come to a compromise blend of these two effects is to start
off with the mix - let us say an air content of 1.5 per cent and a slump of
75 mm -   and you add the air entraining agent, deliberately, as it were,
an overdose, which would give more air than is finally required.
Let us say that we get nominally 6 per cent, and some enhancement of
workability, a slump of about 120 mm.   While the superplasticiser is
added, associated with it would be the air release, due to its competition
for adsorption sites and the dispersion effect.   So much so that the net
final air content will now drop - let us say to that level we wanted anyhow,
nominally - say - 4% and the workability will go on increasing - say to 200 mm.

I would suggest that that is the sequence in trying to come to a compromise
blend, rather than adding the superplasticiser first, where it is put in
with a mix that has excessive workability and possibly manifests both bleed
and segregation.

I believe, although I have not seen actual measurements, but I have heard
various opinions, that the bubble size and the bubble spacing factor that may
result as a consequence of this double addition is different to that usually
quoted for a durable and freeze/thaw resistant concrete.   But having said
that, at the same time, and certainly at the CANMET Conference, it was also
implied that whilst there was deviation from the quoted normal values,
the concrete was very durable and very freeze/thaw resistant.   So much so
that some doubt was expressed over the normal bubble size and spacing
factors, and at that time, the A C I Committee on the durability of concrete
intended to look at and review the bubble spacing and size factors in relation
to superplasticised air entrained concrete.   I do not know whether that
took place.

I think there is an incompatibility, though it is an incompatibility that can be readily accommodated. But it is probably, as Mr Moksnes says, all to do with sequence of addition.

J MOKSNES: I can certainly confirm that the mixing sequence, the batching sequence is important. I think we stumbled across this because we had problems getting stable air, and we found that this revised or modified batching procedure, introducing the air into a stiff mix and then superplasticising it, seemed to do the trick.

We got less air, but the air we got was stable. In fact we had far more problems in the past with the ordinary plasticiser and the ordinary Vinsol resin getting stable air.

B HOLLAND (Ballast Nedam Groep, NV., The Netherlands):
Referring to what has just been said about cooking concrete, we are involved in what can only be described as a major project in Saudi Arabia, total value over £1 billion, and the majority of it we have placed using superplasticisers and retarders. This includes mass foundations, or fairly massive foundations where the depth has varied between 1 m and 4 m. The housing system is based on the tunnel form, and we have included all the air conditioning ducts, services, etc., in the walls before pouring, turned round the units in 14 hours, and had a 20 N/mm^2 strength at that time.

I cannot see any problem in using a plasticiser, even at those temperatures in Saudi Arabia.

Really, I have one simple message. To the admixture manufacturers, keep at it. To the contractors, for God's sake look at it. To the consultants, accept that it can be done.

Mr Blundell was asked if he would care to comment on the cost of the last concrete that he showed.

R BLUNDELL: It was not considered of any great importance, but it worked out at about £250 per cubic metre.

CHAIRMAN: As Mr Moksnes said earlier, this was a very small proportion of the total investment in the project.

R BLUNDELL: Oh indeed, yes.

SUMMING UP

K NEWMAN - Chairman (British Ready Mixed Concrete Association, UK): We are coming to the end of what has been a very interesting week organised by the Concrete Society.   The message to me from reading the papers and hearing the contributions from the speakers and also from the floor is that admixtures have finally come of age in the UK.

Whenever we have to face problems which are challenging problems, then everyone gets together: the engineer, the admixture supplier, the contractor, work together to find the correct solution.   But we have seen here that there is more education needed.   Through Professor Kreijger's paper, we are given a much better insight into the mechanics by which admixtures act.   We are now beginning to understand better how admixtures work, although from the discussion that took place yesterday, there are clearly many points still to be resolved as to the exact mechanisms.   As Professor Diamond said, we still do not know all about the hydration of Portland cement alone, without admixtures. But we are gradually getting a better understanding of their action.

What has come across from the various speakers this session, on Case Histories, is the fact that there is a willingness on the part of the admixtures suppliers to look beyond selling so many more litres of their particular product.   Even so they must have been encouraged by the large quantities that have been quoted as being used!   But they show an encouraging willingness to work together with their customers to solve a particular problem.

Several of the speakers have mentioned that there are still many engineers who are adverse to their use. They regard concrete as being a mixture of cement, sand, aggregates and water, which should not be added to in any way.

Certainly there are pressures, both from new developments in the use of concrete, and from energy requirements, for us to examine other materials, such as waste materials, as were listed by Mr Tipler and Mr Dewar. There are now different initiatives for the use of admixtures, and we must react sensibly to these pressures.

If I could make one recommendation to admixture suppliers, they should stop looking nervously over their shoulders and take encouragement from the fact that they have a part to play in concrete today. They should examine more carefully this question of cost. There is a misunderstanding of what is meant by cost, and we have to educate the contractor to look at the whole operation of manufacturing, placing and compaction to see whether or not the use of a particular admixture, a superplasticiser perhaps, which in unit cost terms seems excessively expensive, can produce a more economical and better finished job. Our friends from the precast industry showed very well how this can be done. They examine in detail what they are trying to do and are very happy to use any particular material which will give a finished product as required by the engineer, but one which will be more effectively and economically produced.

OTHER CI80 VOLUMES

Lightweight Concrete

Lightweight aggregates — an updating survey of materials, production technology, innovations and inventions (*M Venuat*) | 1
An update of lightweight aggregate production in UK (*D B Horler*) | 11
Modern methods of cellular concrete structures design (*N I Levin and K M Romanovskaya*) | 23
Aerated light weight concrete — current technology (*G Båve*) | 28
Pelletised lightweight slag aggregates (*J J Emery*) | 36
Properties of hardened lightweight aggregate concrete (*F D Lydon*) | 47
The properties of hardened concrete with lightweight porous aggregates (*Y V Chinenkov, I Volkov and Y M Romanov*) | 63
An international review of the fire resistance of lightweight concrete (*J C M Forrest*) | 73
Thermal conductivity as quality parameter (*G Svanholm*) | 91
The properties of aerated concrete in service (*F N Leitch*) | 97
Design peculiarities of aerated lightweight concrete and structures (*I A Solodukhin*) | 114
Design and detailing considerations of lightweight concrete structures generally (*M E R Little*) | 120
Design considerations for prestressed lightweight aggregate concrete (*B K Bardhan-Roy*) | 125
Design peculiarities of prestressed supporting constructions from concretes on porous aggregates (*N A Kornev, V G Kramar and A A Kudryavtsev*) | 141
The testing of structural lightweight concrete (*J B Newman and T W Bremner*) | 152
Use of electrical conductivity of metallic fibres for the thermal treatment of fresh concrete and for the heating of hardened reinforced concrete (*A M Paillere and J J Serano*) | 172
Place and occasion in architecture (*J A Partridge*) | 182
Physical properties of high strength lightweight aggregate concretes (*T A Holm*) | 187
The economics and use of lightweight concrete in civil engineering structures (*B Bender*) | 205
Economics of lightweight structural concrete in building work (*E R Skoyles*) | 212
Lightweight concrete thermal insulation structures (*M O Mannonen*) | 231
Outstanding applications of lightweight concrete and an appreciation of likely future developments (*J Bobrowski*) | 239
On site and laboratory testing of lightweight aggregate concrete (*M M Virlogeux*) | 261
Lightweight concrete structures, potentialities, limits and realities (*H Bomhard*) | 277

Sprayed Concrete

An introduction to sprayed concrete (*L J Bell*) | 1
Specifications and Codes of Practice for sprayed concrete (*E F Humphries*) | 8
Wet process shotcrete (*G S Littlejohn*) | 18
Dinorwig tunnels and caverns (*E Waller*) | 36
Sprayed concrete in repair and strengthening work (*W B Long*) | 52
Construction using sprayed concrete (*T Ryan*) | 59
Dry mix shotcrete (*G Haag*) | 81

Fibrous Concrete

Review of the present scene (*D J Hannant*) | 1
Steel fibrous concrete — a review of testing procedures (*C H Henager*) | 16
Properties of steel fibre reinforced mortar and concrete (*C D Johnson*) | 29
Properties of GRC (*A J Majumdar*) | 48
Properties and performance of GRC (*B A Proctor*) | 69
Organic reinforcing fibres for cement and concrete (*H Krenchel and H W Jensen*) | 87
Concrete and cement composites reinforced with natural fibres (*D J Cook*) | 99
Precast and sprayed steel fibre concrete (*Å Skarendahl*) | 115
Bulk steel fibre reinforced concrete has arrived in Australia (*W A Marsden*) | 128
Application of steel fiber to refractory reinforcement (*L E Hackman*) | 137
Design and specification of GRC (*M W Fordyce*) | 153
Applications of glassfibre reinforced cement (*J W Smith and T W D Walker*) | 174
Commercial development of alternatives to asbestos sheet products based on short fibres (*N Pedersen*) | 189
Sheets and pipes incorporating polymer film material in a cement matrix (*J Bijen and E Geurts*) | 194

Admixtures

Plasticisers and dispersing admixtures (*P C Kreijger*) | 1
Accelerating admixtures (*S Diamond*) | 17
Studies of the hydration of Portland cement (*D D Double*) | 32
Superplasticised concrete — high workability retention (*R M Edmeades and P C Hewlett*) | 49
Special purpose admixtures (*L H McCurrich, S A Lammiman and M P Hardman*) | 73
Developments — chloride-free accelerators (*M R Rixom*) | 88
Pigments (*M Levitt*) | 96

Admixtures in use; specification and control (*B Mather*)   103

Analysis for admixtures in hardened concrete (*J D Connolly, W G Hime and B Erlin*)   114

High strength mixes in precast concrete — a case history (*H P Taylor and H Clay*)   130

The use of admixtures in extrusion and sliding form machines for prestressed concrete flooring production (*I H Sparrow*)   136

Admixtures in offshore structures (*J Moksnes*)   143

Using admixtures in pumping concrete (*W A Jury*)   158

The use of admixtures in concrete foundations (*Z J Skiwinski and G H Wadhwani*)   172

Applications of superplasticisers worldwide (*R E Kiesler and W H George*)   184